THEIS MADE EASY

New Methods and a Computer Program in Well Hydraulics

by

Michael Kasenow

THEIS MADE EASY

New Methods and a Computer Program in Well Hydraulics

by

Michael Kasenow

Eastern Michigan University

Water Resources Publications

For Information and Correspondence:

Water Resources Publications
P. O. Box 260026, Highlands Ranch, Colorado 80126-0026, USA

THEIS MADE EASY

New Methods and a Computer Program in Well Hydraulics

by

Michael Kasenow

Eastern Michigan University

ISBN Number 0-918334-84-5

U.S. Library of Congress Catalog Card Number: 94-60960

Manufactured in the United States of America

iv

For Tom Straw,
geo-scientist, wetland muck-about, paleo philosopher,
Indiana story-teller, mentor and friend.

TABLE OF CONTENTS

NINE

NOTATION

b: saturated thickness of (aquifer thickness)

B: laminar flow well loss coefficient

C: turbulent flow well loss coefficient

   non laminar flow well loss coefficient

BQ: well loss due to laminar flow

CQ^2:   well loss due to turbulent flow

K: hydraulic conductivity

L_s: length of well screen

n: number of data points (regression analysis)

Q: production well discharge

ΔQ_x: change in discharge (step-drawdown test)

Q/s: specific capacity

r: observation well distance

r_e: effective well radius

r_L: transient limit of the cone of depression

r_o: distance of zero drawdown at steady rate

r_o':   distance of zero drawdown at steady rate (from recovery data)

r_{stpt}: stagnation point

r_w: radius of the pumping well

r: correlation coefficient (regression analysis)

s: drawdown

s':   residual drawdown

s_a: drawdown in the aquifer adjacent to the pumping well

s_c: critical drawdown, theoretical drawdown required before a straight line will plot on a semilog graph

s'_{min}: $= s_{max}$

s_{new}: new drawdown

s_o: zero drawdown criterion for r_L

s_{off}: drawdown when the pump test ended = s_{max}

s_{old}: old drawdown

s_p: drawdown in the pumping well

s_{rec}: recovery at a specified time = $(s-s')_{t'}$

s_t: drawdown at time t

$s_{1/2t}$: drawdown at 1/2 of t relative to s_t.

s_w: drawdown in the pumping well

s':   drawdown corrected for dewatering

$(s-s')$: recovery

$(s-s')_{t'}$: recovery at t'.

s/b: drawdown / aquifer thickness ratio

Δs_x: change in drawdown (step-drawdown test)

Δs: slope on a semilogarithmic, time or distance-drawdown graph

$\Delta s'$: slope on a semilogarithmic residual drawdown or time-recovery graph

$\Delta s'_{rec}$: slope on the time-recovery graph = $\Delta(s-s')$

$\Delta(s-s')$: slope on the time-recovery graph = $\Delta s'_{rec}$

S: storativity

S':   storativity (calculated from residual drawdown or recovery data)

S_y : specific yield

t: time

t':   time of residual drawdown

t_{new}: new time

t_o: time of zero drawdown at steady rate

t'_o: time of zero recovery at steady rate

t_{off}: time of pump test

t_{old}: old time

$(t/t')_o$: origin on a residual drawdown graph (where $\Delta s'$ intersects origin)

T: transmissivity

u: mu, the argument mu, a Theis correction factor

u':   mu relative to residual drawdown

W(u): the well function of u, a Theis correction factor

ONE

THE THEIS TYPE CURVE METHOD

THE THEIS EQUATION (1935): THEORY

The Theis equation can be written as

$$s = \frac{Q}{4\pi T} \int_{\frac{r^2 S}{4Tt}}^{\infty} \frac{e^{-u}\,du}{u} \qquad (1)$$

where

s = drawdown = L
r = observation well distance = L
Q = pumping well discharge = L^3/t
S = storage coefficient = dimensionless
T = transmissivity = L^2/t
t = time since start of pumping = t, and
u = $\dfrac{r^2 S}{4Tt}$ $\qquad (2)$

and the integral expression is given by the series:

$$\int_{u}^{\infty} \frac{e^{-u}}{u}\,du = W(u) = -0.5772 - \ln u + u - \frac{u^2}{2\cdot 2!} + \frac{u^3}{3\cdot 3!} - \frac{u^4}{4\cdot 4!} \cdots$$

where W(u) is the well function or the exponential integral of u.

The Theis equation may be rewritten as

$$s = \frac{QW(u)}{4\pi T}$$

and expressed in common logarithmic form as

$$\log s = [\log(Q/4\pi T)] + \log W(u)$$

$$\log r^2/t = [\log(4T/S)] + \log u.$$

3

DEVELOPMENT OF THE THEIS EQUATION

The following excerpts are from Heath (1987):

"In 1935, C.V. Theis of the New Mexico Water Resources District of the U.S. Geological Survey developed the first equation to include time of pumping as a factor that could be used to analyze the effect of withdrawals from a well. Thus, the **Theis Equation** permitted, for the first time, determination of the hydraulic characteristics of an aquifer before the development of new steady-state conditions resulting from pumping. The importance of this capability may be realized from the fact that, under most conditions, a new steady-state cannot be developed or that, if it can, many months or years may be required."

"The Theis equation applies at all times and places (if the assumptions are met). These assumptions are most nearly met by confined aquifers at sites remote from their boundaries. However, if certain precautions are observed, the equation can also be used to analyze tests of unconfined aquifers."

"The forms of the Theis equation used to determine the transmissivity and storage coefficient are (for consistent units)

$$T = \frac{QW(u)}{4\pi s} \tag{3}$$

$$S = \frac{4Ttu}{r^2} \tag{4}$$

where T is transmissivity, S is the storage coefficient, Q is the pumping well rate, s is drawdown, t is time, r is the distance from the pumping well to the observation well, W(u) is the well function of u, which results from

$$-0.577216 - \log_e u + u - (u^2 / 2 \times 2! + u^3 / 3 \times 3! + u^4 / 4 \times 4! + \cdots)$$

and $u = (r^2 S) / (4Tt)$."

"The form of the Theis equation is such that it cannot be solved directly. To overcome this problem, Theis devised a convenient graphic method of solution that involves the use of a type curve. ... Analysis of aquifer-test data using the Theis equation involves plotting both the type curve and test data on logarithmic graph paper. If the aquifer and the conditions of the test satisfy Theis's assumptions, the type curve has the same shape as the cone of depression along any line radiating away from the pumping well and the drawdown graph at any point in the cone of depression."

"Use of the Theis equation for unconfined aquifers involves two considerations. First, if the aquifer is relatively fine grained, water is released slowly over a period of hours or days, not instantaneously with the decline in head. Therefore, the value of S determined from a short-period test may be too small.

Second, if the pumping rate is large and the observation well is near the pumping well, dewatering of the aquifer may be significant, and the assumption that the transmissivity of the aquifer is constant is not satisfied (Figure 1). The effect of dewatering of the aquifer can be eliminated with the following equation:

5

$$s' = s - (s^2 / 2b) \qquad\qquad (5)$$

where s is the observed drawdown in the unconfined aquifer, b is the aquifer thickness, and s' is the drawdown that would have occurred if the aquifer had been confined (that is, if no dewatering had occurred)."

THE THEIS SOLUTION

The Theis solution (1935) quantifies drawdown in a confined aquifer near a pumping well as a function of pumping rate **(Q)**, distance from the observation well **(r)**, and the time **(t)** at which drawdown or declining head **(s)** is measured. The solution offered by Theis is convenient, but involves the use of two graphs: a type curve and a data curve. Both graphs are logarithmic. To apply this method, pump test data points are plotted on one graph with **drawdown (s)** on the vertical scale vs **time (t)** on the horizontal scale. This produces a curve of data points. This curve is then superimposed on a type curve. The type curve is constructed with **the inverse of the argument of u** on the horizontal axis and **W(u), the well function of u**, on the vertical axis (Figure 2). The overlapping curves are matched --- with the vertical and horizontal axes of both graphs parallel to each other. At a convenient and single point the values of **s, t, W(u), and 1/u** are selected. **W(u)** is the well function of the argument **u**, and can be approximated from infinite series mathematics (page 9). **W(u) and u are correction factors**. These values are then substituted into the Theis equations, which solve for **T** and **S** (page 14) [other methods use r^2/t or $1/r^2$ for the horizontal axis on the data point graph].

6

THE CONE OF DEPRESSION: UNCONFINED AQUIFER

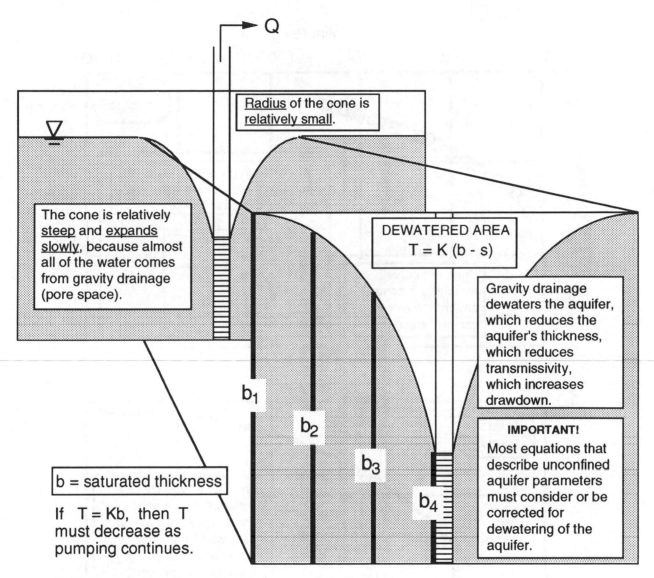

Q

Radius of the cone is relatively small.

The cone is relatively steep and expands slowly, because almost all of the water comes from gravity drainage (pore space).

DEWATERED AREA
$$T = K (b - s)$$

Gravity drainage dewaters the aquifer, which reduces the aquifer's thickness, which reduces transmissivity, which increases drawdown.

IMPORTANT!
Most equations that describe unconfined aquifer parameters must consider or be corrected for dewatering of the aquifer.

b_1

b_2

b_3

b_4

b = saturated thickness

If $T = Kb$, then T must decrease as pumping continues.

If T decreases, then drawdown must increase.

FIGURE 1

THEIS SOLUTION REQUIRES
TWO CURVES: TYPE CURVE AND DATA CURVE

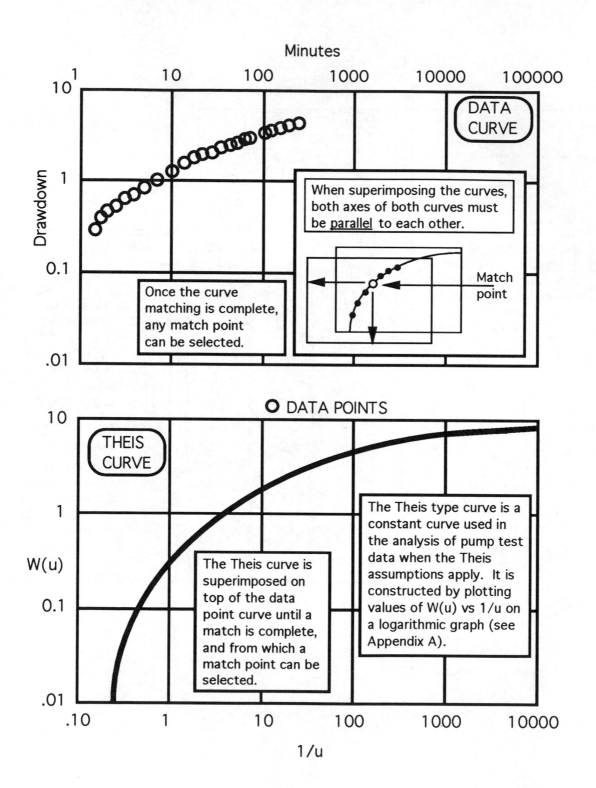

FIGURE 2

THEIS EQUATION: u and W(u)

W(u) is the well function of the argument, u, and can be approximated from infinite series mathematics. The following infinite series can be used to approximate W(u). u can be defined from 1.0 x E-10 to 10.

$$W(u) \approx -0.5772 - \ln(u)$$

$$W(u) \approx -0.5772 - \ln(u) + u$$

$$W(u) \approx -0.5772 - \ln(u) + u - \frac{u^2}{2 \times 2!} + \frac{u^3}{3 \times 3!} - \frac{u^4}{4 \times 4!} + \frac{u^5}{5 \times 5!}$$

$$W(u) \approx -0.5772 - \ln(u) + u - .25u^2 + .0552u^3 - .0098u^4 + .0011u^5$$

$$W(u) \approx \frac{u^4 + 8.573301u^3 + 18.059u^2 + 8.6348u + 0.2678}{u[e^u] \left[u^4 + 9.573301u^3 + 25.633u^2 + 21.1u + 3.9585 \right]}$$

A spreadsheet program such as LOTUS, QUATRO or EXCEL can be used to solve for the above approximations. Numbers defining u should be in the first column and each sequence of approximations in following columns.

THEIS ASSUMPTIONS

The Theis analytical solution considers the nonsteady response of the hydraulic head (groundwater elevation, i.e., drawdown) as an effect from a pumping well tapping a confined aquifer. Application of the Theis solution invokes the following assumptions (Figure 3):

1) Discharge from the pumping well is instantaneous with decline in pressure.
2) The well fully penetrates and is open through the entire extent of the aquifer.
3) The well's radius is very small so that well storage is negligible.
4) Flow to the well screen is radial, horizontal and laminar.
5) The aquifer is homogeneous and isotropic.
6) Aquifer thickness is uniform.
7) The aquifer remains saturated during the entire pumping test.
8) The aquifer is infinite (in areal extent, no areal boundaries).
9) The aquifer is horizontal and bounded above and below by impermeable beds (aquifer is confined).
10) All storage of water within the aquifer comes from the cone of depression (the aquifer is isolated from overlying or underlying leaky aquifers, local recharge, precipitation, irrigation, rivers, lakes and wetlands).

The Theis solution uses two logarithmic graphs. A graph with a constant type curve and a graph with data points relative to a pumping test (Figure 4). Four variables are selected from a match point and utilized in two equations in order to define **T** and **S**. The method is cumbersome, especially when constructed and completed by hand. Semilog graphs are easier to construct and easier to complete, because they require one sheet of semilog graph paper and no match point. In addition, simple groundwater modeling can be applied through the use of algebraic equations. The accuracy of a semilog solution decreases with decreasing pumping time and with increasing observation well distance.

CONFINED AQUIFER WITH SOME
OF THE THEIS ASSUMPTIONS

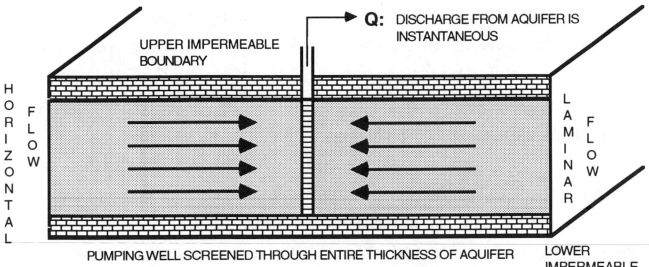

AQUIFER IS INFINITE IN AREAL EXTENT

UPPER IMPERMEABLE BOUNDARY

Q: DISCHARGE FROM AQUIFER IS INSTANTANEOUS

HORIZONTAL FLOW

LAMINAR FLOW

PUMPING WELL SCREENED THROUGH ENTIRE THICKNESS OF AQUIFER

LOWER IMPERMEABLE BOUNDARY

RECTANGULAR AQUIFER; UNIFORM THICKNESS

HOMOGENEOUS

Material is the same throughout the system.

ISOTROPIC

Magnitude of aquifer properties is equal in all directions.

FIGURE 3

11

VALIDITY OF THE THEIS ASSUMPTIONS

The Theis assumptions are important to understand because many analytical equations used in hydrogeology relative to pumping tests are born from the Theis equation. Obviously all of the above assumptions cannot be satisfied for every aquifer test; therefore, the hydrogeologist must understand the nature of the system being explored, and must ascertain the severity of assumption violation in order to render the calculations useful. The validity of each assumption must be evaluated for specific test conditions, but as a general rule, the more important assumptions can be justified as follows.

Most aquifers are not **horizontal, of uniform thickness and homogeneous**, but pumping well effects relative to these assumptions are minor, because they are considered to be **average values** of the aquifer system. **Transmissivity and storativity are not constant** everywhere in an aquifer, they too are considered to be **average values**. Most aquifers are **anisotropic**, but the effect on drawdown is minor when the well screen is constructed so that it fully penetrates the entire aquifer thickness. When the well screen is not fully penetrating, the total screen length open to the aquifer can be substituted for aquifer thickness, but using screen length for aquifer thickness will generally result in aquifer parameters that are lower than actual values. **Partial penetration** problems can be compensated for if the design and location of the observation wells are considered during construction of the pump test. Various mathematical formulas can also be used to correct for partial penetration effects. The **diameter of the pumping well** rarely causes error in pump test results (unless the diameter of the pumping well is excessively large). All aquifers have **areal boundaries**, but many aquifers can be considered **infinite in areal extent** relative to pumping time. If the cone of depression never reaches a boundary, then that boundary can be considered to be at an infinite distance from the pumping well. If the pumping well is near an aquifer boundary, then the results from graphical analysis may be unreliable. **The storage assumption is often the most violated assumption**. Many pump tests have shown that some water pumped from specific aquifers may come from storage external to that aquifer. Methods have been developed to solve for leaky aquifer and recharge boundary conditions. **Instantaneous discharge from aquifer storage does not occur**, but storativity does approach a constant value with increasing pumping time.

THEIS EQUATIONS

3) $T = \dfrac{QW(u)}{4\pi s} = m^2 / time$ or $ft^2 / time$

4) $S = \dfrac{4Ttu}{r^2} = unitless$

> Units must be consistent for equations 3 and 4.
> $Q = L^3 / time : L = m$ or ft

6) $T = \dfrac{114.6QW(u)}{s} = gallons/day/ft$

7) $S = \dfrac{uTt}{1.87r^2} = unitless$

> Units are not consistent for equations 6 and 7.

> Q = gallons/minute
> s = feet
> r = feet
> t = days

8) $T = \dfrac{15.3QW(u)}{s} = ft^2 / day$

> Units are not consistent for equations 8 and 9.

9) $S = \dfrac{Ttu}{360r^2} = unitless$

> Q = gallons/minute
> s = feet
> r = feet
> t = minutes

THEIS EXAMPLE PROBLEM

Theoretically, the Theis matching curve solution applies at all times and places in an aquifer during a pump test when the Theis assumptions are satisfied, but the method is subjective. Error can occur due to manual plotting of the data points and curve manipulation, yet it is superior to most other methods relative to accuracy.

Time vs drawdown data (Lohman, 1972) have been plotted on the data point curve (top graph, Figure 2). Figure 4 demonstrates the matching curve technique.

PUMP TEST DATA

Q = 500 gpm	
r = 400 ft	

TIME (min)	s (feet)
1	0.16
1.5	0.27
2	0.38
2.5	0.46
3	0.53
4	0.67
5	0.77
6	0.87
8	0.99
10	1.12
12	1.21
14	1.26
18	1.43
24	1.58
30	1.70
40	1.88
50	2.00
60	2.11
80	2.24
100	2.38
120	2.49
150	2.62
180	2.72
210	2.81
240	2.88

THEIS EXAMPLE PROBLEM

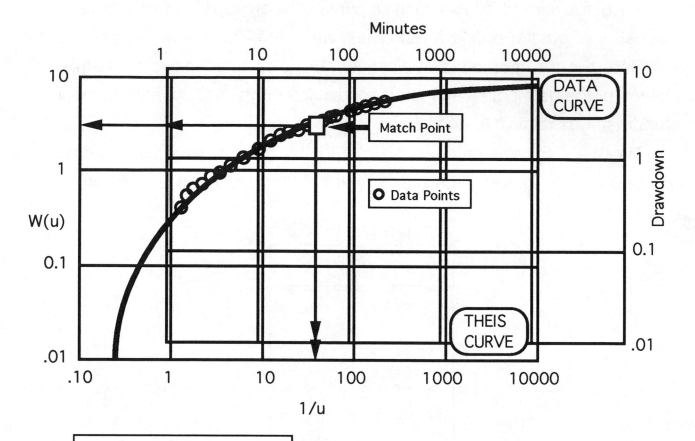

W(u) = 3.7
1/u = 70, u = 0.014
t = 60 min = 0.0417 days
s = 2.11 ft

Select a convenient match point from which drawdown (s), time (t), W(u), and 1/u can be obtained.

Using equations 6 and 7, and the correct units:

T = 100,479 gpd / ft

S = 0.00020

FIGURE 4

16

TWO

THE COOPER-JACOB METHOD

THE COOPER - JACOB EQUATION (1946): THEORY

From equation (2), Cooper and Jacob noted that the value of **u** decreases as the time, **t**, increases.

$$u = \frac{r^2 S}{4Tt}$$

For large values of **t** or small values of **r**, the sum in the series in equation (1) beyond the term **ln u** is negligible;

$$\int_u^\infty \frac{e^{-u}}{u} \, du = W(u) = -0.5772 - \ln u + u - \frac{u^2}{2 \cdot 2!} + \frac{u^3}{3 \cdot 3!} - \frac{u^4}{4 \cdot 4!} \ldots$$

therefore, the Theis equation in the form

$$s = \frac{QW(u)}{4\pi T}$$

can be rewritten as

$$s = Q/4\pi T \left[-0.5772 - \ln(u) \right] \tag{10}$$

$$s = Q/4\pi T \left[\ln(4Tt/r^2 S) - \ln(e^{0.5772}) \right]. \tag{11}$$

For consistent units and time - drawdown analysis

$$s = \left[\left[Q/4\pi T \right] \ln \left[2.3 \, T/r^2 S \right] \right] + \left[Q/4\pi T \right] \ln(t). \tag{12}$$

19

For consistent units and distance - drawdown analysis

$$s = [[Q / 4\pi T] \ln [2.3\ Tt / S]] + [-Q / 2\pi T] \ln (r). \qquad (13)$$

When solving for the value of u where s = 0, and converting to common logarithms, equations (10) and (11) can be rewritten as

$$s = [2.3Q / 4\pi T] \log [2.25\ Tt / r^2 S] \qquad (14)$$

When drawdowns are plotted on semilog graph paper, a straight-line slope occurs when u is sufficiently small. The slope = $[s_2 - s_1 / \log (t_2 / t_1)]$ or $[s_2 - s_1 / \log (r_1 / r_2)]$. If the difference in drawdown is measured over one log cycle, then the slope = Δs and transmissivity for consistent units is related to the first term in equation (14).

$$T = \frac{2.3Q}{4\pi\Delta s} \quad \text{for time - drawdown analysis, and} \qquad (15)$$

$$T = \frac{2.3Q}{2\pi\Delta s} \quad \text{for distance - drawdown analysis.} \qquad (16)$$

When s = 0, then $t = t_o$ or $r = r_o$. The storage coefficient, related to the second term in equation (14), can be expressed as

$$S = \frac{2.25Tt_o}{r^2} \qquad (17)$$

for time - drawdown analysis

and

$$S = \frac{2.25Tt}{r_o^2}$$ (18)

for distance- drawdown analysis.

Where

Q = pumping well discharge = L^3/t
T = transmissivity = L^2/t
t = time duration of pump test = t
t_o = time of zero drawdown = t
r = observation well distance = L
r_o = distance of zero drawdown = L
S = storage coefficient = dimensionless, and
Δs = change in slope over one log cycle = L.

TIME - DRAWDOWN SOLUTION

The Cooper-Jacob (1946) time vs drawdown solution uses the convenience of semilogarithmic graph paper. Cooper and Jacob noted that for **large values of pumping time (t)** or **small values of observation well distance (r)**, time vs drawdown data points will plot as a straight line on semilogarithmic graph paper. The Cooper-Jacob method is only **valid for small values of u**. Utilizing drawdowns that have corresponding **u values less than 0.03** will theoretically result in errors less than 1% relative to the Theis solution (Dawson and Istok, 1991). Some authors are comfortable with u values less than 0.05 because theoretical errors are less than 5%, but as Butler (1957) pointed out, for most practical field situations, **u values should probably not exceed 0.02**. Walton (1988) and May (1963) also recommend u values less than or equal to 0.02.

Errors in T for various values of u (Sheahan, 1967).	u	Error in T (%)
	0.01	1
	0.02	2
	0.05	5
	0.10	10
	0.20	22
	0.50	65

The first few data points are generally ignored when constructing the straight-line slope, because a **steady-rate of drawdowns** generally does not exist at small values of **(t)** (Figure 5). The **slope** of the straight line is proportional to **Q**, and the change in drawdown over one log cycle of time is used to compute **T** and **S**. **Time is labeled on the horizontal or**

TRANSIENT, STEADY-RATE AND STEADY-STATE
GROUNDWATER FLOW TO WELLS

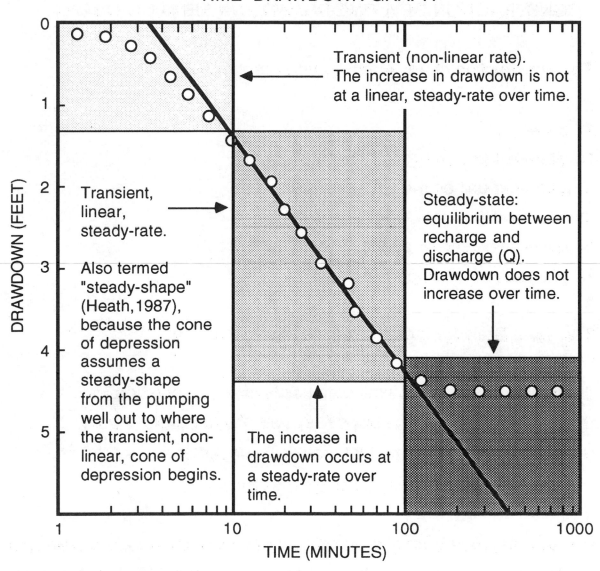

TIME -DRAWDOWN GRAPH

Transient (non-linear rate). The increase in drawdown is not at a linear, steady-rate over time.

Transient, linear, steady-rate.

Also termed "steady-shape" (Heath,1987), because the cone of depression assumes a steady-shape from the pumping well out to where the transient, non-linear, cone of depression begins.

Steady-state: equilibrium between recharge and discharge (Q). Drawdown does not increase over time.

The increase in drawdown occurs at a steady-rate over time.

DRAWDOWN (FEET)

TIME (MINUTES)

FIGURE 5

23

logarithmic axis and drawdown is labeled on the vertical or arithmetic axis. The Theis assumptions apply to the Cooper-Jacob approximation.

CONSTRUCTION OF A TIME-DRAWDOWN SEMILOG GRAPH

The construction of <u>any mathematical graph</u> requires at least:

1) a title,
2) a labeled unit on the x (horizontal) axis,
3) a labeled unit on the y (vertical) axis,
4) source with date,
5) name of person or agency constructing graph,
6) and date of graph construction.

The <u>Time-Drawdown</u> graph will establish (Figure 6):

1) drawdown relative to time data points in an observation well,
2) a "best fit" straight line slope **(Δs)** over one log cycle of time,
3) and the estimated time that drawdown began at steady-rate: **t_o**
   (or time of zero drawdown at steady-rate).

If **r**, the distance from the pumping well to the observation well, and **Q**, the pumping rate are known, then equations (15),(17),(19),(20), (21) and (22) can be used to find **T**, **S** and **K**, (K, if the aquifer thickness is known). The estimated time at which drawdown began **(t_o)** can be estimated by manipulating equations (17),(20) and (22).

TIME - DRAWDOWN EQUATIONS

15) $T = \dfrac{2.3Q}{4\pi\Delta s} = m^2 / \text{time} \quad \text{or} \quad ft^2 / \text{time}$

17) $S = \dfrac{2.25Tt_o}{r^2} = \text{unitless}$

> Units must be consistent for equations 15 and 17.
> $Q = L^3 / \text{time}: \quad L = m \text{ or } ft$

---

19) $T = \dfrac{264Q}{\Delta s} = \text{gallons/day/ft}$

20) $S = \dfrac{0.3Tt_o}{r^2} = \text{unitless}$

> Units are not consistent for equations 19 and 20.

> $Q = \text{gallons/minute}$
> $s = \text{feet}$
> $r = \text{feet}$
> $t_o = \text{days}$

---

21) $T = \dfrac{35Q}{\Delta s} = ft^2 / \text{day}$

22) $S = \dfrac{Tt_o}{640r^2} = \text{unitless}$

> Units are not consistent for equations 21 and 22.

> $Q = \text{gallons/minute}$
> $s = \text{feet}$
> $r = \text{feet}$
> $t_o = \text{minutes}$

THE COOPER - JACOB SEMILOGARITHMIC
APPROXIMATION FOR THE THEIS EQUATION

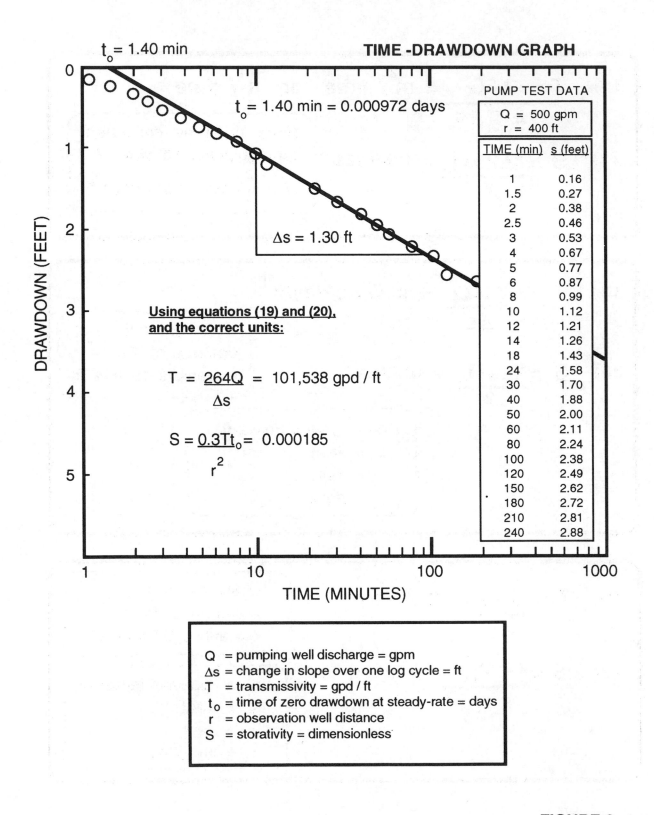

t_o = 1.40 min

TIME -DRAWDOWN GRAPH

t_o = 1.40 min = 0.000972 days

Δs = 1.30 ft

Using equations (19) and (20),
and the correct units:

$$T = \frac{264Q}{\Delta s} = 101,538 \text{ gpd / ft}$$

$$S = \frac{0.3Tt_o}{r^2} = 0.000185$$

DRAWDOWN (FEET)

TIME (MINUTES)

PUMP TEST DATA	
Q = 500 gpm	
r = 400 ft	
TIME (min)	s (feet)
1	0.16
1.5	0.27
2	0.38
2.5	0.46
3	0.53
4	0.67
5	0.77
6	0.87
8	0.99
10	1.12
12	1.21
14	1.26
18	1.43
24	1.58
30	1.70
40	1.88
50	2.00
60	2.11
80	2.24
100	2.38
120	2.49
150	2.62
180	2.72
210	2.81
240	2.88

Q = pumping well discharge = gpm
Δs = change in slope over one log cycle = ft
T = transmissivity = gpd / ft
t_o = time of zero drawdown at steady-rate = days
r = observation well distance
S = storativity = dimensionless

FIGURE 6

DISTANCE-DRAWDOWN SOLUTION

The distance-drawdown solution is similar to the time-drawdown method in its use of semilogarithmic paper, construction, plotting technique and analysis of the change in drawdown, using a straight line slope, over one log cycle. The Theis assumptions and conditions applicable to small values of u also apply. **Distance is labeled on the horizontal or logarithmic axis and drawdown is labeled on the vertical or arithmetic axis.** The slope of the straight line is again proportional to **Q**, and the change in drawdown over one log cycle is used to compute **T** and **S**.

Advantages of the Semilogarithmic Methods:

Simplicity of construction and use when done by hand.

Distance-drawdown solution approximates the outer limit of the cone of depression (r_o) at steady-rate.

Disadvantages of the Semilogarithmic Methods:

Methods should only be used when u is sufficiently small. Unlike the Theis method, the semilogarithmic solutions do not apply at all times and all places in the aquifer when the assumptions are satisfied.

Because of ease in construction, compared to the Theis graphical method, the semilog solutions have been utilized by "lazy" scientists or by groundwater "experts" unaware of the importance of the additional assumption: t must be long enough or r short enough in order for u to be at least ≤ 0.05 (your author prefers u to be ≤ 0.02). Aquifer parameters are often erroneous when this assumption is ignored. Cooper and Jacob stated in their paper, that their method should supplement the Theis graphical solution --- not replace it!

_____

CONSTRUCTION OF A DISTANCE-DRAWDOWN SEMILOG GRAPH

The <u>Distance-Drawdown</u> graph is constructed and used in a similar manner, except the time variable is replaced by distance on the horizontal axis and the slope is constructed into the opposite direction (by convention). t_o is replaced by r_o, which is the distance of the steady-rate limit of the cone of depression.

The <u>Distance-Drawdown</u> graph will establish (Figure 7):

1) drawdowns relative to distance in at least 3 observation wells, measured at the same time,

2) a "best fit" straight line slope (Δs) over one log cycle of distance,

3) and the estimated steady-rate limit of the cone of depression: r_o (or distance where zero drawdown occurs at steady-rate).

If t, the pumping time, and Q, the pumping rate are known, then equations (16),(18),(23),(24),(25) and (26) can be used to find T, S and K (K, if the aquifer thickness is known). The steady-rate limit of the cone of depression (r_o) can be estimated by manipulating equations (18),(24) and (26).

DISTANCE VS DRAWDOWN EQUATIONS

16) $T = \dfrac{2.3Q}{2\pi\Delta s} = m^2/\text{time}$ or ft^2/time

18) $S = \dfrac{2.25Tt}{r_o^2} = \text{unitless}$

> Units must be consistent for equations 16 and 18.
> $Q = L^3/\text{time}: L = m$ or ft

23) $T = \dfrac{528Q}{\Delta s} = \text{gallons/day/ft}$

24) $S = \dfrac{0.3Tt}{r_o^2} = \text{unitless}$

> Units are not consistent for equations 23 and 24.

> $Q = \text{gallons/minute}$
> $s = \text{feet}$
> $r_o = \text{feet}$
> $t = \text{days}$

25) $T = \dfrac{70Q}{\Delta s} = ft^2/\text{day}$

26) $S = \dfrac{Tt}{640r_o^2} = \text{unitless}$

> Units are not consistent for equations 25 and 26.

> $Q = \text{gallons/minute}$
> $s = \text{feet}$
> $r_o = \text{feet}$
> $t = \text{minutes}$

DISTANCE - DRAWDOWN SEMILOGARITHMIC SOLUTION

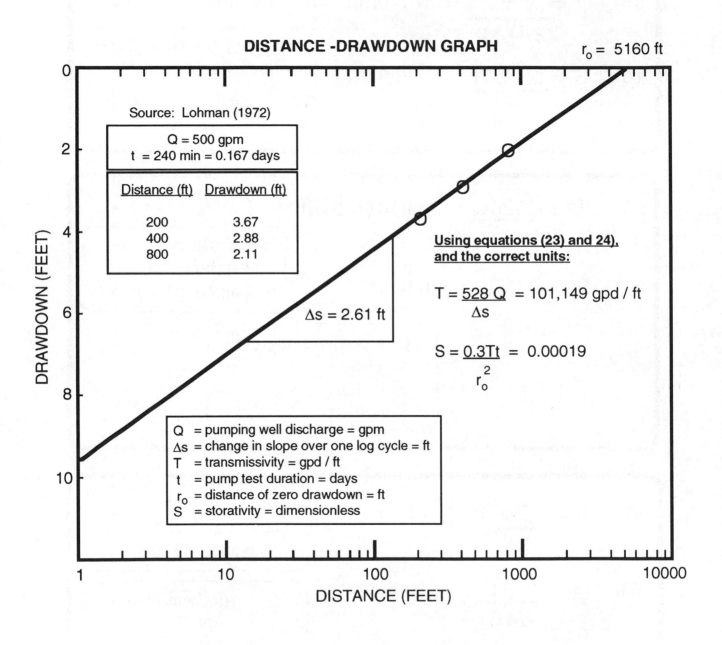

DISTANCE -DRAWDOWN GRAPH

$r_o = 5160$ ft

Source: Lohman (1972)

Q = 500 gpm
t = 240 min = 0.167 days

Distance (ft)	Drawdown (ft)
200	3.67
400	2.88
800	2.11

$\Delta s = 2.61$ ft

Using equations (23) and (24), and the correct units:

$$T = \frac{528\,Q}{\Delta s} = 101{,}149 \text{ gpd / ft}$$

$$S = \frac{0.3Tt}{r_o^2} = 0.00019$$

Q = pumping well discharge = gpm
Δs = change in slope over one log cycle = ft
T = transmissivity = gpd / ft
t = pump test duration = days
r_o = distance of zero drawdown = ft
S = storativity = dimensionless

DRAWDOWN (FEET)

DISTANCE (FEET)

FIGURE 7

30

THREE

OGDEN'S METHOD

L. Ogden (1965) developed a simple and relatively accurate method to approximate transmissivity in production or observation wells utilizing a **single drawdown and the Theis solution.** The Theis equations are manipulated and equated to solve for **uW(u).** **u** is then identified from a table, and transmissivity is calculated utilizing the Theis equation that operates with **u**. The method has seen little use, because a convenient u, uW(u) table was never developed. Your author has completed that task (so have Kruseman and deRidder, 1990). The table in Appendix A can be used with the following equations:

$$\mathbf{uW(u) = \frac{1.87Ssr^2}{114.6Qt} = dimensionless.} \tag{27}$$

and

$$\mathbf{T = \frac{1.87Sr^2}{ut} = gpd\,/\,ft} \tag{28}$$

where

Q = the pumping rate in gallons per minute,

r = the observation well distance

    or

    pumping well radius in feet,

s = the drawdown in feet,

t = the pumping time in days, and

S = the storage coefficient, which is dimensionless.

All of the variables can be measured during a pump test, except for the storage coefficient, which must be assumed.

If the radius of the pumping well is considered to be r = 1.00 foot, then equations (27) and (28) can be simplified to the following equations:

$$uW(u) = \frac{(0.01632)Ss}{Qt} \qquad \text{and} \qquad (29)$$

$$T = \frac{1.87S}{ut} = gpd / ft. \qquad (30)$$

Hurr (1966) also derived equations (27) and (28) using different logic.

Ogden's method is appropriate for specific capacity **(Q / s)** data, but it can also be used as a pump test field equation when the proper storage coefficient is assumed. Theis (1963), Brown (1963) and Lohman (1972) contend that a S_y of .2 is a sufficient assumption for water table aquifers, because .2 is the median value within the unconfined storage range. Patchick (1967) and Hurr (1966) use .1 in their solution methods, and the mean of 18 field values provided by Prickett (1965) supports their choice. Reasonable results can be obtained when using the following general rule:

For gravel and coarse grain sand assume S_y = .2

For medium to fine grain sand assume S_y = .1

Theis (1963) and Brown (1963) favor **.0001** as a valid storage assumption for confined aquifers. Ogden (1965), Patchick (1967), and

34

Kasenow (1993) use **.0005** in their solution methods. Both values are reasonable storage assumptions when considering **confined aquifers**.

According to Lohman (1972):

"In examining logs of wells or test holes in confined aquifers, or in measuring sections of exposed rocks that dip down beneath confining beds to become confined aquifers, the storage coefficient may be estimated by multiplying the aquifer thickness **(b)** in feet by **1 x 10 $^{-6}$**."

$$S_{estimated} = b (10^{-6}) \tag{31}$$

Kasenow (1993) provides an extensive table that supports equation (31). He also provides equations that correct for dewatering around a production well assuming 100% well efficiency [Equation (5) is generally not appropriate for unconfined production well drawdown when s ≥ 25% of the aquifer's saturated thickness.] (Figure 8).

CORRECTING FOR DEWATERING AROUND A PUMPING WELL IN A WATER TABLE AQUIFER: EXAMPLE PROBLEM

A pump test was completed in a water table aquifer **26 feet thick**. The drawdown data in observation wells was collected over a **240 minute period** and the pumping rate was constant at **1162.64 gpm**. After equation (5) was used to correct observation well drawdown data, the **transmissivity was estimated to be about 154,700 gpd / ft,** and the **storage coefficient was estimated to be about .22** (U.S. Department of the Interior, 1981).

CORRECTING PRODUCTION WELL DRAWDOWN FOR DEWATERING IN A WATER TABLE AQUIFER

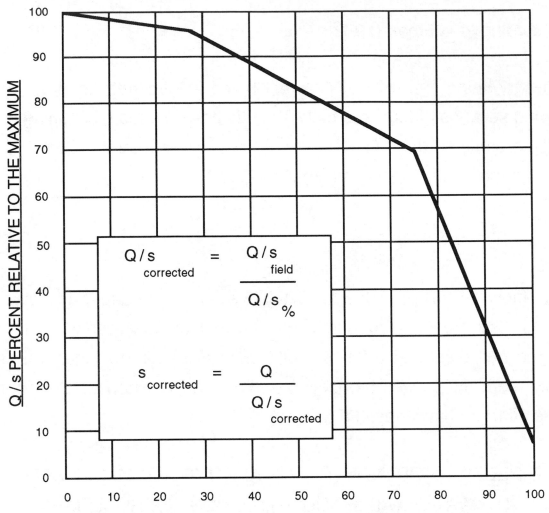

PERCENT DRAWDOWN: DRAWDOWN / AQUIFER THICKNESS = **s / b**

TO CORRECT Q / s FOR DEWATERING OF THE PUMPING WELL USE THE FOLLOWING EQUATIONS:

s / b ratio < 25%

(32) $1 - [(s/b)(.19)]$ = relative Q / s as a percent

s / b ratio ≥ 25% AND ≤ 75%

(33) $1 - [((s/b) - .20))(.54)]$ = relative Q / s as a percent

s / b ratio > 75%

(34) $1 - [((s/b) - .64))(1.24)]$ = relative Q / s as a percent

FIGURE 8

36

The **drawdown in the pumping well was estimated to be 9.95 feet uncorrected**. Equation (5) was used to correct the drawdown, which was determined to be around **8.05 feet**. Using the corrected drawdown, **specific capacity** was estimated to be about 144.4 gpm/ft of drawdown. The aquifer parameters were again calculated. **Specific yield remained about the same; estimated to be about .24, but transmissivity was estimated to be about 175,350 gpd / ft.**

Estimate transmissivity with the help of Figure 8;
Assume a well radius of 1.00:

$s / b = (9.95 \text{ ft} / 26.0 \text{ ft}) = .38$

The aquifer s / b ratio ≥ 25% and ≤ 75%; therefore equation (33) is appropriate, and

$Q / s \% = 1 - [(s / b) - .20)(.54)] = .903$

$Q / s_{corrected} = \dfrac{Q / s_{field}}{Q / s \%} = \dfrac{116 \text{ gpm/ ft}}{.903} = 128.5 \text{ gpm / ft}$

$S_{corrected} = \dfrac{Q}{Q / s_{corrected}} = \dfrac{1162.64 \text{ gpm}}{128.5 \text{ gpm / ft}} = 9.04 \text{ feet}$

To estimate transmissivity use equations (27) and (28):

$uW(u) = \dfrac{1.87 S s r^2}{114.6 Q t} = \dfrac{(1.87)(.22)(9.04 \text{ feet})(1)^2}{(114.6)(1162.64 \text{ gpm})(.1667 \text{ days})}$

uW(u) = .000167

u from Appendix A is about = .0000160

$$T = \frac{1.87Sr^2}{ut} = \frac{(1.87)(.22)(1)^2}{(.0000160)(.1667 \text{ days})}$$

T = 154,244 gpd / ft

The **T** calculated from **Q/s** data compares favorably with the **T** estimated from observation well data: error < 1% (Table 1).

Table 1. Results of methods used to correct production well drawdown for dewatering.

Method	Q/s (gpm/ft)	s(ft)	T(gpd/ft)	Error(%)
Observation well data	129.4	9.00	154,700	-----
Q/s correction by Q/s % method (Kasenow, 1993)	128.5	9.04	154,244	1% <
Q/s correction using equation (5)	144.4	8.05	175,350	12%

FOUR

RECOVERY METHOD

THE RECOVERY METHOD

One way to confirm the results of a pump test is to measure the rise of water level in the pumping well or observation well after the pump test has been concluded and the pump is turned off. Theoretically, this rise or drawup should be a mirror image of the drawdown, it rarely is, but it does offer a reflection worth measuring. Often the calculated parameters are very good approximations relative to each other, which adds evidence to the data bank.

The recovery method (Theis, 1935; Jacob, 1963), in some sense, is a cost effective method, considering that the production well and observation wells are already constructed --- and there is no pumped water to dispose of. It serves as both a check and alternative to the pump test.

The recovery method can only be used after a constant rate pumping test, and only for a time-recovery analysis. The natural recovery of groundwater in observation wells does not allow for a distance-recovery test.

After a specific capacity test in a pumping well has run its course, the time-recovery analysis should be utilized. The recovery method is much more accurate for production well measurements relative to a time-drawdown test, because there are no pump vibrations or turbulence to contend with. **Transmissivity** can be estimated using production well recovery data, but the **true storage coefficient cannot**, because the **effective radius** of the production well is often unknown. The storage coefficient can be estimated using observation well recovery data, but current graphical efforts are often avoided because they are tedious and laborious. Two and often three graphs are constructed to obtain t_o', which is utilized in Cooper-Jacob approximation equations. New methods have been developed that estimate the storage coefficient utilizing single graph information from which only transmissivity has commonly been calculated; they will be demonstrated later in this chapter.

Before proceeding terms should be defined:

Residual drawdown (s') is the measured water level in a well after a pump test has been concluded --- or --- the **drawup**.

Recovery (s-s') is the difference between the drawdown and drawup, but **s** in the parentheses is the **theoretical drawdown** for a well at a particular time **if the pump test had continued**, and **s'** is the residual drawdown (graph 2, Figure 9).

t = time since pump test started.

t' = time since pump test stopped or **recovery began**.

(t / t') = a unitless ratio.

The general equation that will be used to define **transmissivity** is

$$T = \frac{264\,Q}{\Delta s'} \qquad \text{where} \qquad (35)$$

T = transmissivity = gpd / ft,
Q = pump test pumping rate = gpm, and
$\Delta s'$ = is the change in residual drawdown
over one semilog cycle of (t / t').

RECOVERY CURVES

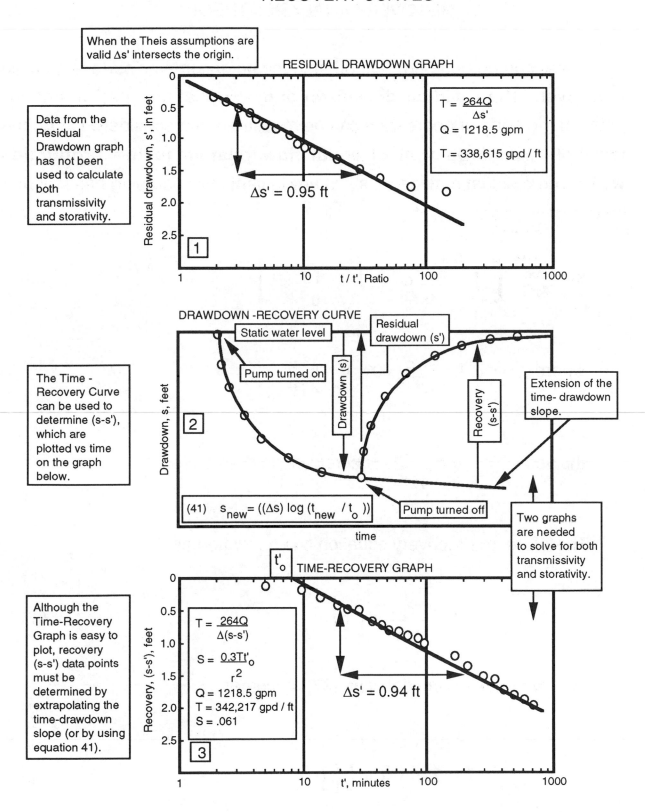

When the Theis assumptions are valid Δs' intersects the origin.

Data from the Residual Drawdown graph has not been used to calculate both transmissivity and storativity.

RESIDUAL DRAWDOWN GRAPH

$T = \dfrac{264Q}{\Delta s'}$

Q = 1218.5 gpm

T = 338,615 gpd / ft

Δs' = 0.95 ft

Residual drawdown, s', in feet

t / t', Ratio

1

DRAWDOWN -RECOVERY CURVE

The Time - Recovery Curve can be used to determine (s-s'), which are plotted vs time on the graph below.

Static water level

Pump turned on

Drawdown (s)

Residual drawdown (s')

Recovery (s-s')

Extension of the time- drawdown slope.

$(41) \quad s_{new}= ((\Delta s) \log (t_{new} / t_o))$

Pump turned off

Two graphs are needed to solve for both transmissivity and storativity.

Drawdown, s, feet

time

2

TIME-RECOVERY GRAPH

Although the Time-Recovery Graph is easy to plot, recovery (s-s') data points must be determined by extrapolating the time-drawdown slope (or by using equation 41).

t'_o

$T = \dfrac{264Q}{\Delta (s-s')}$

$S = \dfrac{0.3Tt'_o}{r^2}$

Q = 1218.5 gpm

T = 342,217 gpd / ft

S = .061

Δs' = 0.94 ft

Recovery, (s-s'), feet

t', minutes

3

FIGURE 9

43

A well can be pumped, shut off, and the potentiometric surface allowed to recover. The **residual drawdown** or **drawup** at any time and at any point on the cone of depression can be measured and considered to be the result of a **recharge well of equal flow relative to the production well**. The residual drawdown, s', at any instant after pumping has stopped can be defined as:

$$s = \frac{Q}{4\pi T} \left[\int_u^\infty \frac{e^{-u}}{u} du - \int_{u'}^\infty \frac{e^{-u'}}{u'} du' \right] \tag{36}$$

where
$$u = \frac{r^2 S}{4Tt} \quad \text{and} \quad u' = \frac{r^2 S'}{4Tt'},$$

the value
$$u' = \frac{r^2 S'}{4Tt'} \quad \text{decreases as } t' \text{ increases.}$$

Therefore, the recovery equation can be written as

$$T = \frac{Q}{4\pi s'} \ln \left[\frac{t}{t'} \right], \tag{37}$$

and when $Q = $ gpm equation (37), becomes

$$T = \frac{114.6Q}{s'} \ln \left[\frac{t}{t'} \right]. \tag{38}$$

Converting to the base-10 log or using the Cooper - Jacob approximation equation, the residual drawdown at any time can be expressed as

$$s' = \frac{264Q}{T} \left[\log [0.3Tt / r^2S] - [\log 0.3Tt' / r^2S'] \right] \tag{39}$$

and when assuming S = S', equation (39) can be simplified to

$$s' = \frac{264Q}{T} \log [t/t']. \tag{40}$$

s' is proportional to, **t/t'**, and can be plotted against the unitless ratio on semilog graph paper. A straight line slope can be constructed and transmissivity calculated using equation (35):

$$T = \frac{264\,Q}{\Delta s'} . \tag{35}$$

_____

TRANSMISSIVITY AND THE RECOVERY METHOD

Transmissivity can be calculated using groundwater recovery and one of four different solutions: residual drawdown graph method, time-recovery graph method, equation approximation method or the slope approximation method.

RESIDUAL DRAWDOWN GRAPH METHOD

1) Make four columns that contain the following data:

    t, t', (t / t') and s'.   **See Table 2 and related graph.**

2) Construct the residual drawdown graph on semilog paper,
    s' vs (t / t'). The s' values should be plotted on the vertical axis
    and the (t / t') values on the horizontal axis (graph 1, Figure 9).

3) Construct a best-fit slope.

4) Find Δs' over one semilog cycle.

5) Calculate **T** using equation (35):

$$T = \frac{264Q}{\Delta s'} = gpd / ft$$

Table 2: residual drawdown data

Pump test results: **T = 338,045 gpd/ft; S = 0.063**
Observation well 1, **r = 100 ft, Q = 1218.5 gpm.**
Source: Ground Water Manual (1981), pp 120-121.

Time since pump test started t = minutes	Time since pumping stopped t' = minutes	Ratio t / t'	Residual drawdown s' = feet
800	0	0.0	1.86
805	5	161.0	1.78
810	10	81.0	1.64
815	15	54.3	1.53
820	20	41.0	1.45
825	25	33.3	1.37
830	30	27.7	1.32
840	40	21.0	1.22
850	50	17.0	1.15
860	60	14.3	1.09
870	70	12.4	1.03
880	80	11.0	0.97
890	90	9.88	0.94
900	100	9.00	0.90
910	110	8.27	0.87
920	120	7.67	0.85
980	180	5.44	0.70
1040	240	4.33	0.61
1100	300	3.67	0.54
1160	360	3.22	0.49
1220	420	2.90	0.46
1280	480	2.67	0.40
1340	540	2.48	0.36
1400	600	2.33	0.36
1460	660	2.21	0.34
1520	720	2.11	0.31
1600	800	2.00	0.29

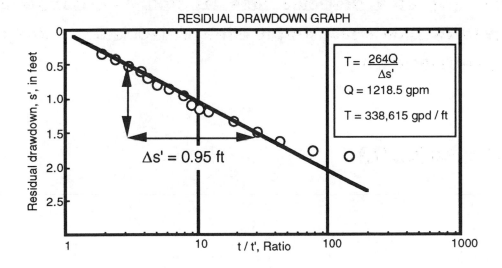

RESIDUAL DRAWDOWN GRAPH

$$T = \frac{264Q}{\Delta s'}$$

Q = 1218.5 gpm

T = 338,615 gpd / ft

Δs' = 0.95 ft

When the Theis assumptions are in harmony with the recovery test, $\Delta s'$ will intersect the origin at 0,1 --- also remember that t/t' is a unitless ratio; therefore, t_o' cannot be identified on the residual drawdown graph, making it difficult to calculate the storage coefficient. This method is sufficient for both observation and production well data.

TIME- RECOVERY GRAPH METHOD

After **residual drawdown data** have been collected from the **observation well**, a second graph, the **time-recovery graph**, can be constructed using differences between extended theoretical drawdowns relative to the pump test and residual drawdowns **(s - s')** (graph 2, Figure 9). Two more columns need to be added to Table 2, which results in Table 3: the theoretical pump test drawdown column for t, and a column for recovery. The time-recovery graph is constructed with **(s - s')** on the vertical axis and **t'** on the horizontal axis. Although more work is required to construct this graph, its major advantage is the identification of **t'$_o$**, which can be used to calculate the storage coefficient. To obtain the extended drawdown **(s)** at a projected time **(t)** from the **Cooper-Jacob time-drawdown pump test graph**, either extrapolate the straight line slope or use equation (41).

$$s_{new} = (\Delta s) \log (t_{new} / t_o) \tag{41}$$

TABLE 3: Recovery data. T from the pump test = 338,045 gpd/ft. S = 0.063.

Time since pump test started t = minutes	Time since pumping stopped t' = minutes	Ratio t / t'	Residual drawdown s' = feet	Pump test s extended	Recovery (s - s')
Recovery Data: observation well 1, **r = 100 ft Q = 1218.5 gpm**. Source: Ground Water Manual (1981), pp 120-121.					
800	0	0.0	1.86	1.86	0.00
805	5	161.0	1.78	1.86	0.08
810	10	81.0	1.64	1.86	0.22
815	15	54.3	1.53	1.86	0.33
820	20	41.0	1.45	1.87	0.42
825	25	33.3	1.37	1.87	0.50
830	30	27.7	1.32	1.87	0.55
840	40	21.0	1.22	1.88	0.66
850	50	17.0	1.15	1.88	0.73
860	60	14.3	1.09	1.89	0.80
870	70	12.4	1.03	1.89	0.86
880	80	11.0	0.97	1.90	0.93
890	90	9.88	0.94	1.90	0.96
900	100	9.00	0.90	1.91	1.01
910	110	8.27	0.87	1.91	1.04
920	120	7.67	0.85	1.92	1.07
980	180	5.44	0.70	1.94	1.24
1040	240	4.33	0.61	1.97	1.36
1100	300	3.67	0.54	1.99	1.45
1160	360	3.22	0.49	2.01	1.52
1220	420	2.90	0.46	2.03	1.57
1280	480	2.67	0.40	2.05	1.65
1340	540	2.48	0.36	2.07	1.71
1400	600	2.33	0.36	2.09	1.73
1460	660	2.21	0.34	2.11	1.77
1520	720	2.11	0.31	2.12	1.81
1600	800	2.00	0.29	2.15	1.86

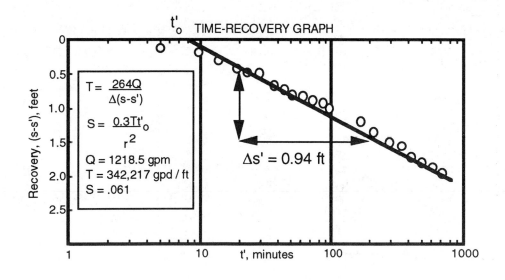

TIME-RECOVERY GRAPH

$T = \dfrac{264Q}{\Delta(s-s')}$

$S = \dfrac{0.3Tt'_o}{r^2}$

Q = 1218.5 gpm
T = 342,217 gpd / ft
S = .061

$\Delta s' = 0.94$ ft

Recovery, (s-s'), feet

t', minutes

49

If the Theis assumptions are valid, equation (40) can be used to solve for T using a residual drawdown (s') at any time after pumping has stopped (t'). In practice t' should be ≥ about 20 minutes. Select s' and t' values at logical increments of time, solve for T, and take the average. This method does not need a graph and can be used conveniently in the field. Examples 1 and 2 demonstrate the accuracy of the **equation approximation method.** Example 1 pump test: T = 338,045 gpd/ft and S = 0.063.

Table 4: Equation Approximation Method -- Example 1

Observation well 1, **r = 100 ft, Q = 1218.5 gpm.**
Source: Ground Water Manual (1981), pp 120-121.

$$T = \frac{264Q}{s'} \log \left[\frac{t}{t'} \right]$$

Time since pump test started t = minutes	Time since pumping stopped t' = minutes	Ratio t / t'	Residual drawdown s' = feet	
800	0	0.0	1.86	Ave T = 342,375 gpd/ft
805	5	161.0	1.78	
810	10	81.0	1.64	
815	15	54.3	1.53	
820	20 √	41.0	1.45	T at t' 20 min = 357,798 gpd/ft
825	25	33.3	1.37	
830	30	27.7	1.32	
840	40	21.0	1.22	
850	50	17.0	1.15	
860	60	14.3	1.09	
870	70	12.4	1.03	
880	80	11.0	0.97	
890	90	9.88	0.94	
900	100 √	9.00	0.90	T at t' 100 min = 341,071 gpd/ft
910	110	8.27	0.87	
920	120	7.67	0.85	
980	180	5.44	0.70	
1040	240	4.33	0.61	
1100	300	3.67	0.54	
1160	360	3.22	0.49	
1220	420	2.90	0.46	
1280	480	2.67	0.40	
1340	540	2.48	0.36	
1400	600 √	2.33	0.36	T at t' 600 min = 328,257 gpd/ft
1460	660	2.21	0.34	
1520	720	2.11	0.31	
1600	800	2.00	0.29	

EQUATION APPROXIMATION METHOD: EXAMPLE 2

Table 5: Equation Approximation Method -- Example 2

Pump test results: **T = 10,950 gpd/ft; S = 0.000017**
Observation well 1, **r = 824 ft, Q = 220 gpm.**
Source: Bruin and Hudson (1955)

$$T = \frac{264Q}{s'} \log \left[\frac{t}{t'}\right]$$

Time since pump test started t = minutes	Time since pumping stopped t' = minutes	Ratio t / t'	Residual drawdown s' = feet	
500	0	0	10.9	Ave T = 10,490 gpd/ft
502	2	251	10.6	
504	4	126	9.7	
506	6	84	9.6	
508	8	63.5	9.1	
510	10	51	8.81	
512	12	42.67	8.42	
514	14	36.71	8.23	
516	16	32.25	8.04	
518	18	28.78	7.85	
520	20 √	26.00	7.76	T at t' 20 min = 10,590 gpd/ft
522	22	23.72	7.37	
524	24	21.83	7.15	
526	26	20.23	6.99	
528	28	18.86	6.97	
530	30	17.67	6.79	
534	34	15.71	6.52	
538	38	14.16	6.35	
546	46	11.87	5.85	
550	50	11.00	5.70	
560	60	9.33	5.35	
565	65	8.69	5.17	
570	70	8.14	5.13	
590	90	6.56	4.58	
600	100 √	6.00	4.41	T at t' 100 min = 10,248 gpd/ft
620	120	5.17	3.98	
630	130	4.85	3.86	
640	140	4.57	3.69	
650	150	4.33	3.62	
660	160	4.13	3.33	
670	170	3.94	3.29	
680	180	3.78	3.26	
770	270	2.85	2.54	
800	300 √	2.67	2.33	T at t' 300 min = 10,632 gpd/ft
830	330	2.52	2.13	
850	350	2.43	2.17	

Results from the **equation approximation method** appear to be reasonable when compared to graphical methods:

Ground Water Manual Example

Method	T (gpd / ft)
Pump test results	338,045
Residual-drawdown graph	338,615
Recovery graph	342,217
Equation approximation	342,375

Gridley Example

Method	T (gpd / ft)
Pump test (Walton, 1962)	10,100
Pump test (Bruin & Hudson, 1955)	10,950
Recovery graph	10,950
Equation approximation	10,490

The slope approximation method is an average of a small sample of point slopes easily calculated using equation (42). The $\Delta s'_{ave}$ is then used with equation (35) to estimate T with a good degree of accuracy (Tables 6 and 7).

The **slope** ($\Delta s'$) at each s' at t' is represented by the quantity:

$$\Delta s' = s' / \log [t/t']. \tag{42}$$

Table 6: Slope Approximation Method -- Example 1

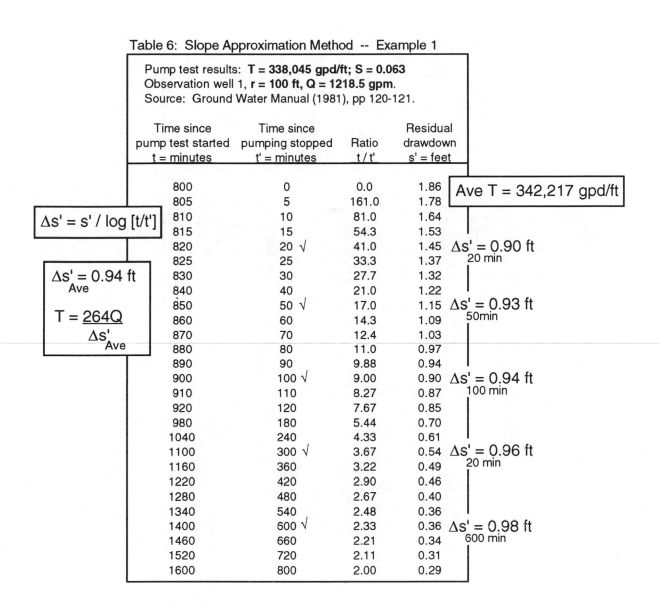

Pump test results: **T = 338,045 gpd/ft; S = 0.063**
Observation well 1, **r = 100 ft, Q = 1218.5 gpm.**
Source: Ground Water Manual (1981), pp 120-121.

Time since pump test started t = minutes	Time since pumping stopped t' = minutes	Ratio t / t'	Residual drawdown s' = feet
800	0	0.0	1.86
805	5	161.0	1.78
810	10	81.0	1.64
815	15	54.3	1.53
820	20 √	41.0	1.45
825	25	33.3	1.37
830	30	27.7	1.32
840	40	21.0	1.22
850	50 √	17.0	1.15
860	60	14.3	1.09
870	70	12.4	1.03
880	80	11.0	0.97
890	90	9.88	0.94
900	100 √	9.00	0.90
910	110	8.27	0.87
920	120	7.67	0.85
980	180	5.44	0.70
1040	240	4.33	0.61
1100	300 √	3.67	0.54
1160	360	3.22	0.49
1220	420	2.90	0.46
1280	480	2.67	0.40
1340	540	2.48	0.36
1400	600 √	2.33	0.36
1460	660	2.21	0.34
1520	720	2.11	0.31
1600	800	2.00	0.29

Ave T = 342,217 gpd/ft

$\Delta s' = s' / \log [t/t']$

$\Delta s'_{Ave} = 0.94$ ft

$T = \dfrac{264Q}{\Delta s'_{Ave}}$

$\Delta s' = 0.90$ ft
20 min

$\Delta s' = 0.93$ ft
50min

$\Delta s' = 0.94$ ft
100 min

$\Delta s' = 0.96$ ft
20 min

$\Delta s' = 0.98$ ft
600min

53

SLOPE APPROXIMATION METHOD: EXAMPLE 2

Table 7: Slope Approximation Method -- Example 2

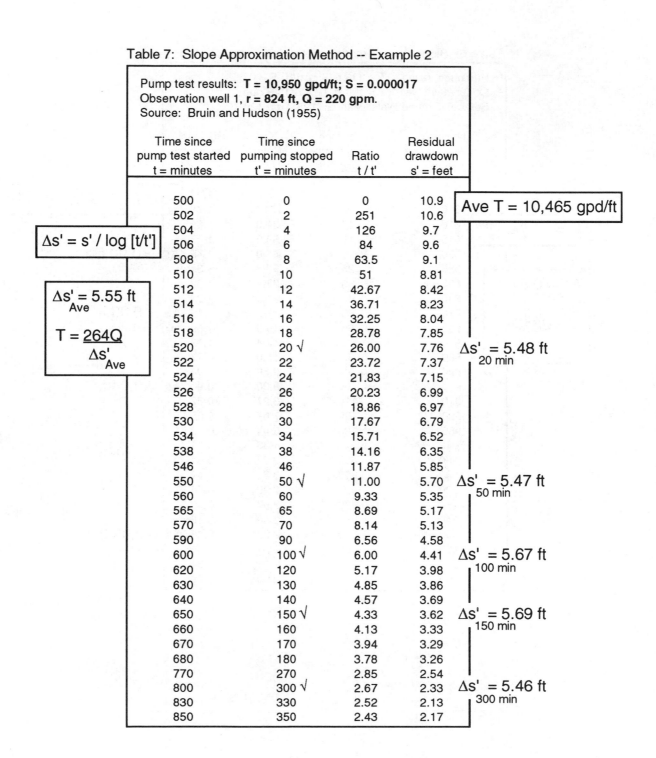

Pump test results: **T = 10,950 gpd/ft; S = 0.000017**
Observation well 1, **r = 824 ft, Q = 220 gpm**.
Source: Bruin and Hudson (1955)

Time since pump test started t = minutes	Time since pumping stopped t' = minutes	Ratio t / t'	Residual drawdown s' = feet
500	0	0	10.9
502	2	251	10.6
504	4	126	9.7
506	6	84	9.6
508	8	63.5	9.1
510	10	51	8.81
512	12	42.67	8.42
514	14	36.71	8.23
516	16	32.25	8.04
518	18	28.78	7.85
520	20 √	26.00	7.76
522	22	23.72	7.37
524	24	21.83	7.15
526	26	20.23	6.99
528	28	18.86	6.97
530	30	17.67	6.79
534	34	15.71	6.52
538	38	14.16	6.35
546	46	11.87	5.85
550	50 √	11.00	5.70
560	60	9.33	5.35
565	65	8.69	5.17
570	70	8.14	5.13
590	90	6.56	4.58
600	100 √	6.00	4.41
620	120	5.17	3.98
630	130	4.85	3.86
640	140	4.57	3.69
650	150 √	4.33	3.62
660	160	4.13	3.33
670	170	3.94	3.29
680	180	3.78	3.26
770	270	2.85	2.54
800	300 √	2.67	2.33
830	330	2.52	2.13
850	350	2.43	2.17

$\Delta s' = s' / \log [t/t']$

$\Delta s'_{Ave} = 5.55$ ft

$$T = \frac{264Q}{\Delta s'_{Ave}}$$

Ave T = 10,465 gpd/ft

$\Delta s' = 5.48$ ft
20 min

$\Delta s' = 5.47$ ft
50 min

$\Delta s' = 5.67$ ft
100 min

$\Delta s' = 5.69$ ft
150 min

$\Delta s' = 5.46$ ft
300 min

The slope approximation method appears to offer good results when compared to other methods that estimate T from recovery data. This too can be utilized as a field equation. Simplicity of use and accuracy are advantages that make this method a viable alternative to graphical analysis. Subjective interpretation relative to slope construction is also eliminated.

STORAGE COEFFICIENT AND THE RECOVERY METHOD

It has been assumed since 1935, when Charles Theis first introduced his transient solution to the hydrogeological world, that the storage coefficient (S) can not be estimated from observation well residual drawdown data. In recent years methods have been developed that offer promising results. Case, Pidcoe and Fenske (1974) offer a series of equations that eventually result in both T and S using only residual drawdown data. Berg (1975) and Vanderberg (1975) use a least sum of squares approach to estimate T and S in leaky confined systems using only residual drawdown data. Bardsley, Sneyd and Hill (1980) improve upon least squares parameter estimation for both pump test drawdown and residual drawdown data --- again, estimating both T and S. Ulrick (1989) offers a program that computes T and S using residual drawdown data and sensitivity analysis. The above authors offer viable methods that give good results compared to T and S obtained from only pump test data, but the disadvantage relative to all five methods is the complicated mathematics involved. Computer methods are needed to apply their work in the practical world.

Methods have been derived that need only a hand-held calculator and common sense; some require graphs, some do not. The purpose of this section is to offer these methods and to explain their advantages and disadvantages.

I: Bruin and Hudson (1955)

Bruin and Hudson were one of the first authors to show how the Cooper-Jacob semilogarithmic method can be used to define the storage coefficient using recovery data. Their method has already been explained above and the constructed graph is again presented below. Review pages 48 and 49 and you will discover that this method is

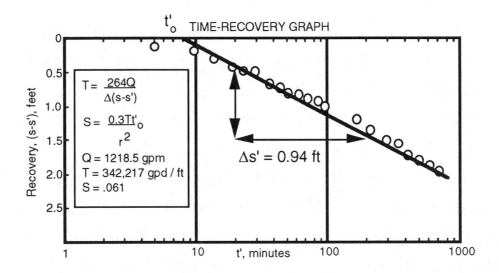

dependent upon the slope of the semilog time-drawdown pump test graph --- **a disadvantage** --- because any errors that occur constructing the pump test graph will be applied to the recovery - time graph. This method has often been ignored by researchers because of its dependence upon pump test data to calculate recovery, and the laborious effort applied to obtain the needed data.

II: Groundwater Manual Equation (1981)

An alternative to the Bruin - Hudson method is equation (43):

$$S = \frac{2.25\,(Tt'/\,r^2)}{\log^{-1}\left[\frac{(s\text{-}s')_{t'}}{(\Delta s')_{rec}}\right]} \quad \text{or} \quad S = \frac{0.3(Tt'/\,r^2)}{\log^{-1}\left[\frac{(s\text{-}s')_{t'}}{(\Delta s')_{rec}}\right]} \quad (43)$$

where, for consistent units,

		where,	
S = storage coefficient		S = dim	
T = transmissivity		T = gpd / ft	
s = pumping period drawdown projected to t'		s = ft	
s' = residual drawdown at t'		s' = ft	
$(s\text{-}s')_{t'}$ = recovery at (t')		$(s\text{-}s')_{t'}$ = ft	
t' = time after pumping stopped = time of s'		t' = days	
t = pump test time		t = days	
r = observation well distance		r = ft	
$\Delta s'_{rec}$ = slope of the recovery-time graph, and		$\Delta s'_{rec}$ = ft	
$\log^{-1}$ = antilog.		$\log^{-1}$ = antilog	

Equation (43) has the advantage of using a single recovery point that falls on or near $\Delta s'_{rec}$ to calculate S. Like the Bruin-Hudson method, it is also dependent upon the slope of the time-drawdown pump test graph to calculate (s-s'); therefore, it is subject to projecting errors from that graph into the result of the equation. Later in this discussion your author will improve upon equation (43). For now, equation (43), as it is currently used, is shown below:

TABLE 8: Recovery data. T from the pump test = 338,045 gpd/ft. S = 0.063.

Recovery Data: observation well 1, **r = 100 ft Q = 1218.5 gpm**
Source: Ground Water Manual (1981), pp 120-121.

Time since pump test started t = minutes	Time since pumping stopped t' = minutes	Ratio t / t'	Residual drawdown s' = feet	Pump test s extended	Recovery (s - s')

$$(43) \quad S = \frac{2.25\,(Tt'/r^2)}{\log^{-1}\left[\dfrac{(s-s')_{t'}}{(\Delta s')_{rec}}\right]} = \frac{2.25[(45,857\ \text{ft}^2/\text{day})(0.0625\,\text{day})\ /\ (100\ \text{ft})^2]}{\log^{-1}\left[\dfrac{(0.96\ \text{ft})}{(0.94\ \text{ft})}\right]} = 0.061$$

840	40	21.0	1.22	1.88	0.66	
850	50	17.0	1.15	1.88	0.73	
860	60	14.3	1.09	1.89	0.80	
870	70	12.4	1.03	1.89	0.86	
880	80	11.0	0.97	1.90	0.93	
890	90	9.88	0.94	1.90	0.96	√
900	100	9.00	0.90	1.91	1.01	
910	110	8.27	0.87	1.91	1.04	
920	120	7.67	0.85	1.92	1.07	
980	180	5.44	0.70	1.94	1.24	

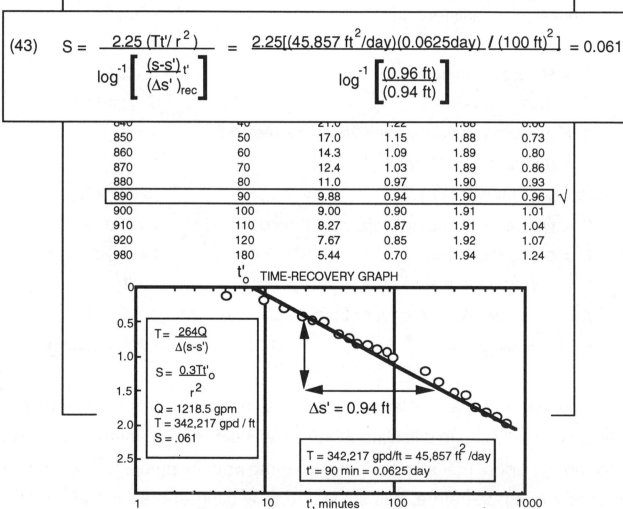

TIME-RECOVERY GRAPH

$$T = \frac{264Q}{\Delta(s-s')}$$

$$S = \frac{0.3Tt'_o}{r^2}$$

Q = 1218.5 gpm
T = 342,217 gpd / ft
S = .061

$\Delta s' = 0.94$ ft

T = 342,217 gpd/ft = 45,857 ft^2/day
t' = 90 min = 0.0625 day

t', minutes

58

The Ground Water Manual equation and the solution offered by Bruin and Hudson should only be used with late recovery-time data, because they are both slope dependent on $\Delta s'_{rec}$.

The next four equations solve for the storage coefficient using only observation well residual drawdown data. All four equations are independent of the semilog time-drawdown pump test Δs; therefore, **errors cannot be projected from the pump test graph to the residual drawdown graph --- eliminating a possible source of error**. The equations do depend upon the last drawdown relative to the transient pump test, which is also the first or minimum residual drawdown or zero point of recovery:

$$S_{\text{pump test maximum}} = s'_{\text{minimum}} = 0.00_{(s-s')}.$$

III: Ballukraya and Sharma (1991)

Ballukraya and Sharma were the first investigators to offer a viable, easy to use equation that estimates the storage coefficient using observation well residual drawdown data. The equation was derived assuming $S = S'$ using the Cooper-Jacob approximation; therefore it is subject to the same restrictions. **Equation (44) should only be used with late residual drawdowns**. When used in this manner, the equation offers good results and is easy to use. In the same paper, Ballukraya and Sharma offer an equation that can correct residual drawdown data to obtain $S = S'$. In reality, the equation is not necessary, because current technology cannot show that $S = S'$, but it does show that S approximates S', which is what realists hope to achieve when conducting a recovery test.

$$S = \frac{2.25Tt}{r^2[t_2/(t_2-t)]^n} \qquad \text{or} \qquad S = \frac{0.3Tt}{r^2[t_2/(t_2-t)]^n} \qquad (44)$$

where, for consistent units,

S = storage coefficient

T = transmissivity

t = pump test time or time of s_{max}

s_{max} = maximum transient
  pump test drawdown

t' = time of s'

s' = residual drawdown, and

$t_2 = (t + t')$

r^2 = observation well distance

$n = s_{max}/s'$.

where,

S = dim

T = gpd / ft

t = days

s_{max} = ft

t' = days

s' = ft

t_2 = days

r^2 = ft

$n = s_{max}/s'$

THE BALLUKRAYA AND SHARMA METHOD FOR DETERMINING THE STORAGE COEFFICIENT USING RESIDUAL DRAWDOWN DATA

Table 9: residual drawdown data

Pump test results: **T = 338,045 gpd/ft; S = 0.063**
Observation well 1, **r = 100 ft, Q = 1218.5 gpm.**
Source: Ground Water Manual (1981), pp 120-121.

Time since pump test started t = minutes	Time since pumping stopped t' = minutes	Ratio t/t'	Residual drawdown s' = feet
800	0	0.0	1.86
860	60	14.3	1.09
870	70	12.4	1.03
880	80	11.0	0.97
890	90	9.88	0.94 √
900	100	9.00	0.90
910	110	8.27	0.87
920	120	7.67	0.85
980	180	5.44	0.70
1040	240	4.33	0.61

$$(44) \quad S = \frac{2.25Tt}{r^2 [t_2/(t_2-t)]^n} = \frac{2.25(45{,}374 \text{ ft}^2/\text{day})(0.5556 \text{ day})}{(100)^2 [0.618/(0.618 \text{ day} - 0.5556 \text{ day})]^{(1.86 \text{ ft}/0.94 \text{ ft})}} = 0.061$$

$t = 800 \text{ min} = 0.5556 \text{ day};\ t_2 = 890 \text{ min} = 0.618 \text{ day};\ T = 338{,}615 \text{ gpd/ft} = 45{,}374 \text{ ft}^2/\text{day}$

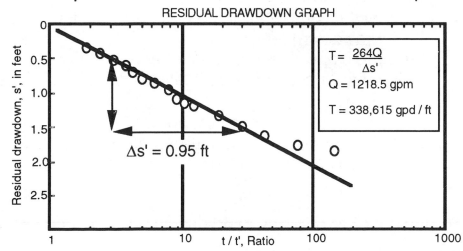

RESIDUAL DRAWDOWN GRAPH

$\Delta s' = 0.95$ ft

$T = \dfrac{264Q}{\Delta s'}$

$Q = 1218.5$ gpm

$T = 338{,}615$ gpd / ft

Residual drawdown, s', in feet

t / t', Ratio

IV: t'_o and the Storage Coefficient Using s' and t'

By observing graphs 1 and 3 (Figure 9) it should be easy to see that the slope of the recovery graph, for practical applications, is equal to the slope of the residual drawdown graph. This is a common sense assumption. The slope does not change using a semilog solution unless T changes (or a boundary effect occurs). Equations derived by Kasenow (1993) use this relationship to solve for recovery and combine both graphs into a single unit that solves for t'_o (see Appendix C for derivation and example).

$$s_{rec} = s_{off} + [\Delta s' [\log((t_{off} + t') / (t_{off}))]] - s' \qquad (45)$$

$$\log t'_o = - \frac{[s_{off} + [\Delta s' [\log((t_{off} + t') / (t_{off}))]] - s']}{\Delta s'} + \log t' \qquad (46)$$

take antilog, $= t'_o$ min.

Where
s_{rec} = recovery at t'
s_{off} = the drawdown immediately after the pumping well has been turned off (or last transient drawdown),
$\Delta s'$ = the slope of the residual drawdown graph,
t_{off} = time duration of pump test (or time of last transient drawdown),
s' = the residual drawdown, and
t' = time since pump was turned off relative to s',
t'_o = time of zero recovery.

Tables 10 and 11 offer good evidence showing that recovery can be described by equation (45). Data from Table 12 is used to demonstrate equation (46).

62

ANALYZING RECOVERY DATA:
EQUATION (45) --- EXAMPLE 1

TABLE 10: Recovery calculated using equation (45).

Recovery Data: observation well 1, **r = 100 ft**
Q = 1218.5 gpm. Pump test results: T = 338,045 gpd / ft; S = .063
Source: Ground Water Manual (1981), pp 120-121.

$$(45) \qquad s_{rec} = s_{off} + [\Delta s' [\log ((t_{off} + t') / (t_{off}))]] - s'$$

Time since pump test started t = minutes	Time since pumping stopped t' = minutes	Ratio t / t'	Residual drawdown s' = feet	Pump test s extended	Recovery extending time vs s graph (s - s')	Recovery using equation (45) (s - s')
800	0	0.0	1.86	1.86	0.00	0.00
805	5	161.0	1.78	1.86	0.08	0.08
810	10	81.0	1.64	1.86	0.22	0.23
815	15	54.3	1.53	1.86	0.33	0.34
820	20	41.0	1.45	1.87	0.42	0.42
825	25	33.3	1.37	1.87	0.50	0.50
830	30	27.7	1.32	1.87	0.55	0.56
840	40	21.0	1.22	1.88	0.66	0.66
850	50	17.0	1.15	1.88	0.73	0.74
860	60	14.3	1.09	1.89	0.80	0.80
870	70	12.4	1.03	1.89	0.86	0.86
880	80	11.0	0.97	1.90	0.93	0.93
890	90	9.88	0.94	1.90	0.96	0.96
900	100	9.00	0.90	1.91	1.01	1.01
910	110	8.27	0.87	1.91	1.04	1.04
920	120	7.67	0.85	1.92	1.07	1.07
980	180	5.44	0.70	1.94	1.24	1.24
1040	240	4.33	0.61	1.97	1.36	1.36
1100	300	3.67	0.54	1.99	1.45	1.45
1160	360	3.22	0.49	2.01	1.52	1.52
1220	420	2.90	0.46	2.03	1.57	1.57
1280	480	2.67	0.40	2.05	1.65	1.65
1340	540	2.48	0.36	2.07	1.71	1.71
1400	600	2.33	0.36	2.09	1.73	1.73
1460	660	2.21	0.34	2.11	1.77	1.77
1520	720	2.11	0.31	2.12	1.81	1.81
1600	800	2.00	0.29	2.15	1.86	1.86

TABLE 11: Recovery calculated using equation (45).

Recovery Data: observation well 1, **r = 824 ft**
Q = 220 gpm. Pump test results: T = 10,950 gpd / ft; S = .000017
Source: Bruin and Hudson (1955).

$$(45) \qquad s_{rec} = s_{off} + [\Delta s' [\log ((t_{off} + t') / (t_{off}))]] - s'$$

Time since pump test started t = minutes	Time since pumping stopped t' = minutes	Ratio t / t'	Residual drawdown s' = feet	Pump test s extended	Recovery extending time vs s graph (s - s')	Recovery using equation (45) (s - s')
500	0	0	10.90	10.90	0.00	0.00
502	2	251	10.60	10.90	0.30	0.31
504	4	126	9.70	10.90	1.20	1.22
506	6	84	9.60	10.90	1.30	1.33
508	8	63.5	9.10	10.90	1.80	1.84
510	10	51	8.81	10.91	2.10	2.13
512	12	42.67	8.42	10.92	2.50	2.53
514	14	36.71	8.23	10.93	2.70	2.73
516	16	32.25	8.04	10.94	2.90	2.93
518	18	28.78	7.85	10.95	3.10	3.13
520	20	26.00	7.76	10.96	3.20	3.23
522	22	23.72	7.37	10.97	3.60	3.63
524	24	21.83	7.15	10.98	3.83	3.85
526	26	20.23	6.99	10.99	4.00	4.03
528	28	18.86	6.97	11.00	4.03	4.06
530	30	17.67	6.79	11.01	4.22	4.24
534	34	15.71	6.52	11.03	4.51	4.53
538	38	14.16	6.35	11.05	4.70	4.72
546	46	11.87	5.85	11.08	5.23	5.25
550	50	11.00	5.70	11.10	5.40	5.42
560	60	9.33	5.35	11.15	5.80	5.81
565	65	8.69	5.17	11.17	6.00	6.01
570	70	8.14	5.13	11.19	6.06	6.07
590	90	6.56	4.58	11.28	6.70	6.70
600	100	6.00	4.41	11.32	6.91	6.91
620	120	5.17	3.98	11.40	7.42	7.42
630	130	4.85	3.86	11.44	7.58	7.57
640	140	4.57	3.69	11.48	7.79	7.78
650	150	4.33	3.62	11.52	7.90	7.88
660	160	4.13	3.33	11.56	8.23	8.21
670	170	3.94	3.29	11.59	8.30	8.28
680	180	3.78	3.26	11.63	8.37	8.35
770	270	2.85	2.54	11.94	9.40	9.35
800	300	2.67	2.33	12.04	9.71	9.65
830	330	2.52	2.13	12.13	10.00	9.94
850	350	2.43	2.17	12.19	10.02	9.95

Table 12: residual drawdown data

Pump test results: **T = 338,045 gpd/ft; S = 0.063**
Observation well 1, r = 100 ft, Q = 1218.5 gpm.
Source: Ground Water Manual (1981), pp 120-121.

Time since pump test started t = minutes	Time since pumping stopped t' = minutes	Ratio t / t'	Residual drawdown s' = feet
800	0	0.0	1.86

(46) $- \dfrac{[s_{off} + [\Delta s' \,[\log\,((t_{off} + t') \,/\, (t_{off}\,))]] - s']}{\Delta s'} + \log t' \;=\; \log t'_o \;\Rightarrow\; \text{antilog} \;=\; t'_o \;=\; \min / 1440 \;=\; \text{day}$

$- \dfrac{[1.86\,\text{ft} + [.95\,\text{ft}\,[\,\log\,((890\,/\,800))]] - .94\,\text{ft}]}{.95\,\text{ft}} + \log 90\,\min \;=\; 0.9395 \;\Rightarrow\; \text{antilog} = 8.70\,\min \;=\; 0.00604\,\text{day}$

850	50	17.0	1.15
860	60	14.3	1.09
870	70	12.4	1.03
880	80	11.0	0.97
890	90	9.88	0.94	√
900	100	9.00	0.90
910	110	8.27	0.87
920	120	7.67	0.85
980	180	5.44	0.70
1040	240	4.33	0.61

$S = \dfrac{0.3T\,t'_o}{r^2}$

$\boxed{S = 0.061}$

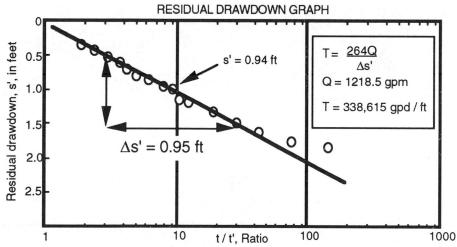

RESIDUAL DRAWDOWN GRAPH

Residual drawdown, s', in feet

s' = 0.94 ft

Δs' = 0.95 ft

$T = \dfrac{264Q}{\Delta s'}$

Q = 1218.5 gpm

T = 338,615 gpd / ft

t / t', Ratio

Equation (46) has the advantage of offering a familiar component used in the Cooper-Jacob approximation solution, t'_o, which allows for a familiar solution to define S (Table 12). Different late residual drawdowns and corresponding t' values will, for most practical considerations, match the mean for S. **Late recovery data allows for a best fit slope. Any residual drawdown can be used that falls on or is directly adjacent to $\Delta s'$** (Table 13). For most purposes equation (46) offers good results when the Theis assumptions are satisfied (Table 14).

Table 13. "Theis Without Graphs" computer program results showing the storage coefficient for data points that fall on or are adjacent to $\Delta s'$. Data is the same as that used in Table 12 (see Table 2).

t' (min)	S (dim)
50	0.059
60	0.060
70	0.060
80	0.058
90	0.061
100	0.061
110	0.062
120	0.065
180	0.062
240	0.064
300	0.064
360	0.065
420	0.072
480	0.060
540	0.054

Reported Mean = 0.062

The "Theis Without Graphs" computer program calculates the mean storage coefficient for all s' values at t' that fall on or are directly adjacent to $\Delta s'$. The result from Table 13 is comparable to previous solution methods.

TABLE 14. RESULTING STORAGE COEFFICIENTS: HISTORICAL DATA COMPARED TO EQUATION (46) USING ALL RESIDUAL DRAWDOWNS THAT FALL ON $\Delta s'$ AND AT A SINGLE POINT [$s' = $ (or nearest to) $0.5s_{off}$]

	Pump Test		Recovery		Residual DD	(All Points)	($s' = 0.5s_{off}$)
Source	T	S	T	S	T	*S	S
1**	338,045	.063	340,087	.062	338,615	.062	.058
2	89,355	.000206	91,762	.00017	92,524	.00018	.00018
3	10,950	.000017	10,950	.000017	10,561	.000017	.000017
4	50,000	.000200	50,000	.000200	50,677	.000190	.000190
5	15,700	.002540	-----	-----	16,838	.002300	.002200
6	334,074	.000250	-----	-----	331,494	.000300	.000300
7	---	-----	12,006	.000082	12,215	.000077	.000073
8	10,000	.0051	10,200	.0036	10,568	.0034	.0036
9	12,614	.000015	11,200	.000023	12,959	.000022	.000026
10	52,800	.0079	49,159	.0065	57,846	.0032	.0032
11	54,831	.0013	45,987	.0018	57,311	.0015	.0016
12	11,143	.0011	14,459	.0014	11,646	.0011	.0028

* "Theis Without Graphs" computer program results.
**Data recalculated by your author using regression analysis. Source $T = 345,765$ gpd / ft and $S = .07$.

Source
1 = Groundwater Manual, (1981)   Q = 1218.5 gpm, r = 100 ft
2 = Todd (1980)   Q = 458.75 gpm, r = 196.86 ft
3 = Bruin and Hudson (1955)   Q = 220 gpm, r = 824 ft
4 = Brown (1953)   Q = 500 gpm, r = 500 ft
5 = Bruin and Hudson (1955)   Q = 250 gpm, r = 12.5 ft
6 = Bruin and Hudson (1955)   Q = 1760 gpm, r = 1270
7 = Ulrick's Sensitivity Analysis (1989) , California.   Q = 650 gpm, r = 285 ft
8 = Groundwater and Wells (1986), Johnson Division.   Q = 200 gpm, r = 50 ft
9 = Village of Columbiaville, Michigan (1989).   Q = 350 gpm, r = 147.42 ft
10 = Village of Pinckney, Michigan (1990).   Q = 540 gpm, r = 50 ft
11 = Village of Pinckney, Michigan (1990).   Q = 540 gpm, r = 120 ft
12 = Village of Dexter, Michigan (1991)   Q = 250 gpm, r = 132 ft

V: Equation (43): New and Improved

As previously stated, equation (43) is prone to accepting errors produced in the construction and use of a semilog time-drawdown pump test graph, which is probably why it has seen limited use in the past. Equation (43) can be adjusted to calculate storage coefficients using only residual drawdown data:

assume

$$\Delta s'_{\text{time recovery graph}} = \Delta s'_{\text{residual drawdown graph}},$$

calculate $(s-s')_{t'}$ using equation (45),

$$s_{rec} = (s-s')_{t'} = s_{off} + [\Delta s' [\log((t_{off} + t') / (t_{off}))]] - s' , \tag{45}$$

and use the T calculated from the residual-drawdown graph.

Substitute these values into equation (43), which can be rewritten as

$$S = \frac{2.25 \, (Tt'/ r^2)}{\log^{-1}\left[\frac{(s_{rec})}{(\Delta s')} \right]} \quad \text{or} \quad S = \frac{0.3 \, (Tt'/ r^2)}{\log^{-1}\left[\frac{(s_{rec})}{(\Delta s')} \right]} \tag{47}$$

Equation (47) is independent of the semilog time-drawdown pump test slope; therefore, any errors that would have been projected from that graph have been eliminated.

68

Equation (47) gives similar results as the example below demonstrates:

$T = 45,374 \text{ ft}^2 / \text{day}$

$\Delta s' = .95 \text{ ft}$

$s_{off} = 1.86 \text{ ft}$

$t = 800 \text{ min} = 0.5556 \text{ day}$

$s' = .94 \text{ ft}$

$t' = 90 \text{ min} = 0.0625 \text{ day}$

$r = 100 \text{ ft}$

$s_{rec} = 1.86 \text{ ft} + [.95 \text{ ft} [\log ((890 / 800))]] - .94 \text{ ft} = 0.964 \text{ ft}$

$$S = \frac{2.25 [(45,374 \text{ ft}^2 / \text{day})(0.0625 \text{ day})] / (100)^2}{\log^{-1} [0.964 \text{ ft} / .95 \text{ ft}]} = 0.062 \qquad (47)$$

The answer is comparable to the previous estimations of S.

VI: r_o' and the Storage Coefficient Using s' and t'

r_o' can be approximated with $\Delta s'$ from the residual drawdown graph and $s'_{minimum}$, which is equal to $s_{maximum}$ from the pump test; this produces equation (48):

$$\log r_o' = [s'_{min} / 2\Delta s'] + \log r_{obs} => \text{antilog} = r_o' \qquad (48)$$

where $r_{obs} = $ the observation well distance in the same unit,

and $r_o' = $ the steady-rate limit of the cone of depression.

After r_o' has been estimated, and depending upon desired units, any of the semilog distance-drawdown equations that solve for the storage coefficient can be used. The example below demonstrates this method using the same data as before:

$T = 43,374$ ft^2 / day $= 338,615$ gpd / ft

$\Delta s' = .95$ ft

$S_{off} = S_{max} = s'_{min} = 1.86$ ft

$t_{pump\ test} = t_{zero\ recovery} = 800$ min $= 0.5556$ day

$s' = .94$ ft

$t' = 90$ min $= 0.0625$ day

$r = 100$ ft

$\log r_o' = [s'_{min} / 2\Delta s'] + \log r_{obs} \Rightarrow antilog = r_o' = $ ft   (48)

$\log r_o' = [1.86$ ft $/ 2(.94$ ft$)] + \log 100$ ft $= 2.979$, antilog $= 952.80$ ft

$S = 0.3Tt / (r_o')^2$ (7)

$S = [0.3(338,615$ gpd /ft$)(.5556$ day$)] / (952.80$ ft$)^2 = 0.062$

This method has the advantage of solving for both the steady-rate cone of depression distance and the storage coefficient. It is also independent of any semilog pump test Δs and offers familiar constants and equations. It has the disadvantage of being more dependent upon the pump test when compared to previous residual drawdown methods, because it uses a single s', which is always the maximum pump test s.

Common sense should be used when applying equation (44), (46) or (47). **Residual drawdowns that fall on $\Delta s'$ offer the most accurate results**. If no residual drawdown falls on $\Delta s'$ (which is unlikely), use s'

70

values that are directly adjacent to Δs'. The above equations are derived from the Cooper-Jacob approximation; therefore, **late residual drawdown data should be used** --- and --- again --- these should fall on or be adjacent to your constructed and subjective Δs'.

IMPORTANT!

The value s_{off}, used in equation (46) to find t'_o, **must be a transient value --- not steady-state.** If the pump test has continued into steady-state, then select the last transient drawdown and its corresponding time, and assume that the transient pump test ended at that interval.

THE RELATIONSHIP BETWEEN Δs' AND THE ORIGIN (0,1)
OF THE RESIDUAL-DRAWDOWN GRAPH

When the Theis assumptions apply the slope of the residual drawdown graph passes through the origin (0,1). Often the slope does not pass through the origin. This may occur due to boundary effects (Driscoll, 1986) or variations in storativity (Jacob, 1963). According to Jacob:

"The apparent average S in the vicinity of a pumped well is often greater during the drawdown period than during the subsequent recovery period. In unconfined or semiconfined aquifers, this difference in S results from the hysteresis of the capillary fringe and from the envelopment of air bubbles by the rising water table. In confined aquifers, the difference results from the consolidation of deposits during pumping, especially in newly developed aquifers."

The methods previously described that solve for S' during the recovery period should probably be used when the S/S' ratio is greater than 0.50 and

71

less than 2.0. The upper limit is based upon Jacob's examples (1963); the lower limit is the inverse of the upper limit. **The S/S' ratio can be determined from the x-intercept on the residual drawdown graph, which is on the log(t/t') axis.** When the S/S' ratio is less than or greater than the above limits, one or more of the Theis assumptions has probably been violated; therefore, an inaccurate storage coefficient is likely to result. Transmissivity can usually be determined from $\Delta s'$ regardless of the difference between the pump test and recovery storage values (the S/S' ratio) (Jacob, 1963).

Equation (49) can be used to determine the degree at which $\Delta s'$ intersects the origin at 1.00 on a residual drawdown graph. Equation (49) is especially helpful when trying to determine the interception of the slope at a point where $\Delta s' < 1.00$.

$$\log (S / S') = (-s' / \Delta s') + \log (t / t') \text{ ---> antilog} = S / S' \text{ ratio} \qquad (49)$$

where s' = the residual drawdown that falls on $\Delta s'$ at (t / t')
and $\Delta s'$ = the slope of the residual drawdown graph.
The probability that a Theis assumption may have been violated
and the storage coefficient erroneous increases when the S/S' ratio is
less than 0.50 or greater than 2.0.

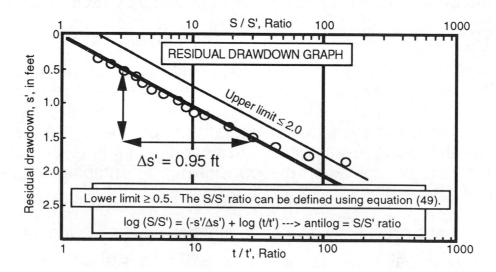

72

FIVE

A SIMPLE METHOD TO SOLVE THE THEIS EQUATION WITHOUT THE THEIS CURVE

THE THEIS SOLUTION WITHOUT GRAPHS

SHEAHAN'S SOLUTION: THEORY

Equating the Theis equation for two drawdowns, a drawdown at a convenient time (s_t) and a drawdown at half the time relative to the original time $(s_{1/2t})$, results in a dimensionless index value that can be used to identify a u and W(u) value for (s_t):

Transmissivity for the same system can be calculated by using

$$T = 114.6QW(u) / s_t \qquad \text{and/or} \qquad \text{(6-A)}$$

$$T = 114.6QW(u)_{1/2t} / s_{1/2t}. \qquad \text{(6-B)}$$

Equations (6-A and 6-B) can be equated. $W(u)_{1/2t}$ can then be solved and compared to values in any competent u, W(u) table, which show $W(u)_{1/2t} = W(2u)$:

$$(s_{1/2t} / s_t)(W(u)) = W(u)_{1/2t} = W(2u). \qquad \text{(50)}$$

Equation (50) can be rearranged to solve for $I_{u,W(u)}$,

$$I_{u,W(u)} = s_{1/2t} / s_t = W(2u) / W(u). \qquad \text{(51)}$$

$I_{u,W(u)}$ = an index number from which values of u and W(u)
         can be identified.

N. T. Sheahan (1967) was the first investigator to derive equation (51) (Appendix C). He used different logic and labeled his result without definition as Z(u); therefore,

$$Z(u) = s_{1/2t} / s_t = W(2u) / W(u), \text{ and} \qquad \text{(51)}$$

Z(u) = an index number from which u and W(u) can be identified.

Equation (51) shows that for every Z(u) value there is one value of W(u), and therefore, one value of u. An extensive, but easy to use Z(u), u, and W(u) table has been constructed by your author (Appendix A). By solving for the second term in equation (51) a value of **Z(u)** can be defined for s_t, and matching values of **u** and **W(u)** can be identified using Appendix A. The problem is then reduced to solving the Theis equations:

$$T = \frac{114.6Q \, W(u)}{s}$$ where

$$S = \frac{uTt}{1.87r^2}$$

T = transmissivity = gpd / ft,
S = storage coefficient = dim,
s = drawdown = ft
r = observation well distance = ft
t = time of s = days, and
Q = pumping rate = gpm.

The solution is quite simple, because it only requires that drawdowns at **t** and **one-half of t** be known. Z(u) is then calculated and u and W(u) identified. If all of the assumptions relative to the Theis solution are satisfied, **T** and **S** can be solved without the Theis curve.

The Z(u) method offers many advantages over the traditional curve matching method and these advantages will be discussed later.

To apply the Z(u) method simply follow three easy steps:

Step 1

Use equation (51) to find Z(u) for s_t:

$$Z(u) = \frac{s_{1/2t}}{s_t} \tag{51}$$

Step 2

Use the calculated Z(u) value to find matching u and W(u) values from Appendix A.

Step 3

Use the appropriate Theis equations, depending upon units, to solve for T and S:

$$T = \frac{114.6Q}{s_t} W(u) \tag{6}$$

$$S = \frac{uTt}{1.87r^2} \tag{7}$$

Example Problem: Data from Lohman (1972)

TIME (min)	DRAWDOWN (ft)	
1.0	0.16	
1.5	0.27	
2.0	0.38	•
2.5	0.46	
3.0	0.53	•
4.0	0.67	•
5.0	0.77	•
6.0	0.87	•
8.0	0.99	•
10.0	1.12	•
12.0	1.21	•
14.0	1.26	
18.0	1.43	
24.0	1.58	•
30.0	1.70	
40.0	1.88	
50.0	2.00	
60.0	2.11	•
80.0	2.24	•
100.0	2.38	•
120.0	2.49	•
150.0	2.62	
180.0	2.72	
210.0	2.81	
240.0	2.88	•

Q = 500 gpm

r = 400 ft

• = drawdowns at **t** that can be matched to drawdowns at 1/2 of t.

$$Z(u) = \frac{s\ at\ 1/2\ of\ t}{s\ at\ t} = \frac{2.49\ ft}{2.88\ ft} = 0.86458$$

From Appendix A: Best Match

$W(u)$ = 5.11 u = .0034

Results Using Z(u) Method   **s = 2.88 ft**
                                                   t = 240 min

T = 101,667 gpd / ft

S = 0.00019

Results Using The Theis Curve

T = 100,479 gpd / ft

S = 0.00020

Results Using Cooper-Jacob

T = 101,538 gpd / ft

S = 0.00019

Equations (6) and (7) were used
to define T and S in all calculations.

78

The Z(u) method can be used in many ways **to replace or supplement graphical solutions and with confidence that the Theis assumptions apply**.

THEIS: TIME-DRAWDOWN SOLUTION

I) Divide the total pump test time into three or four appropriate and logical increments and solve for T and S using Z(u). If a consistency in T and S remains over time, then the Theis assumptions probably apply. Drawdowns collected and analyzed at about one-third to one-fourth increments of time relative to the total pump test time are usually sufficient (Table 15).

Z(u) METHOD FOR EVALUATING DATA POINTS
AT ONE-THIRD INCREMENTS OF TIME

TABLE 15: Two examples compared against historical data.

Data Source: Lohman (1972): Type Curve = T =101,000 gpd/ft; S = 0.0002; Q = 500 gpm; r = 200 ft

t min	s ft	Z(u)	W(u)	u	T gpd /ft	S
12	1.97					
24	2.36	0.8347	4.140	0.00900	100,518	0.00020
40	2.65					
80	3.04	0.8717	5.380	0.00260	101,406	0.00020
120	3.28					
240	3.67	0.8937	6.510	0.00084	<u>101,641</u>	<u>0.00019</u>
				Mean:	101,188	0.00020

TABLE 15: Continued.

Data Source: Groundwater Manual (1981): Type Curve = T =152,000 gpd/ft
S = .24; Q = 1167 gpm; r = 30 ft. (drawdown corrected for dewatering).

t min	s ft	Z(u)	W(u)	u	T gpd /ft	S
15	.880					
30	1.39	0.6360	1.574	0.1300	151,391	0.247
40	1.62					
80	2.18	0.7414	2.501	0.0480	153,386	0.245
120	2.53					
240	3.13	0.8082	3.526	0.0170	150,464	0.250
				Mean:	151,747	0.247

II)   A second method involves the construction of a slope on semilogarithmic graph paper. If most of the time-drawdown data points fall on Δs, and do not deviate from Δs at late values of time, then the Theis assumptions should be valid and the Z(u) method can be used. This approach allows for solutions using the same graph with both the Theis and Cooper-Jacob methods (Figures 10, 11, 12, 13 and 14), but **Z(u) is more powerful because it can be used to evaluate early drawdown data** --- Cooper-Jacob cannot.

SOLVING THE THEIS EQUATIONS WITHOUT
THE THEIS CURVE: METHOD TWO-A

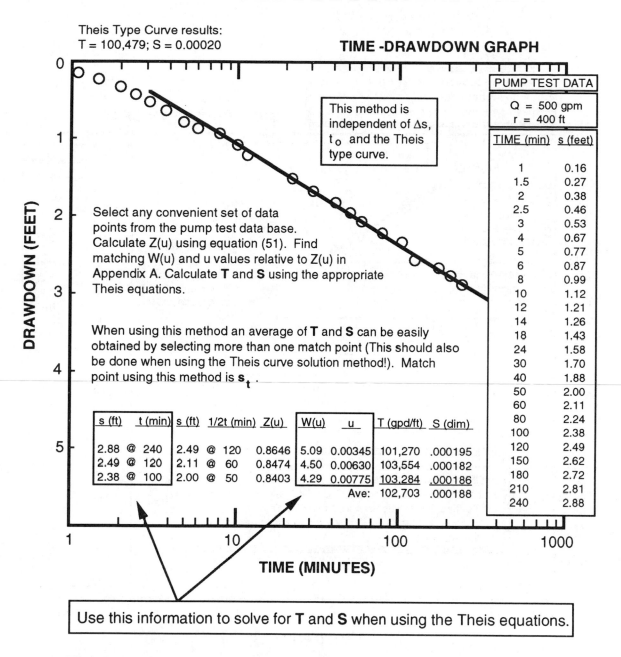

Theis Type Curve results:
T = 100,479; S = 0.00020

TIME -DRAWDOWN GRAPH

This method is independent of Δs, t_o and the Theis type curve.

Select any convenient set of data points from the pump test data base. Calculate Z(u) using equation (51). Find matching W(u) and u values relative to Z(u) in Appendix A. Calculate **T** and **S** using the appropriate Theis equations.

When using this method an average of **T** and **S** can be easily obtained by selecting more than one match point (This should also be done when using the Theis curve solution method!). Match point using this method is s_t .

s (ft)	t (min)	s (ft)	1/2t (min)	Z(u)	W(u)	u	T (gpd/ft)	S (dim)
2.88 @ 240		2.49 @ 120		0.8646	5.09	0.00345	101,270	.000195
2.49 @ 120		2.11 @ 60		0.8474	4.50	0.00630	103,554	.000182
2.38 @ 100		2.00 @ 50		0.8403	4.29	0.00775	103,284	.000186
						Ave:	102,703	.000188

PUMP TEST DATA	
Q = 500 gpm	
r = 400 ft	
TIME (min)	s (feet)
1	0.16
1.5	0.27
2	0.38
2.5	0.46
3	0.53
4	0.67
5	0.77
6	0.87
8	0.99
10	1.12
12	1.21
14	1.26
18	1.43
24	1.58
30	1.70
40	1.88
50	2.00
60	2.11
80	2.24
100	2.38
120	2.49
150	2.62
180	2.72
210	2.81
240	2.88

TIME (MINUTES)

Use this information to solve for **T** and **S** when using the Theis equations.

The slope is constructed in order to validate the Theis assumptions. Drawdown is utilized as a match point.

FIGURE 10

81

Z(u) ADVANTAGE: TYPE CURVE OR
COOPER - JACOB CONSTANTS ARE NOT NEEDED

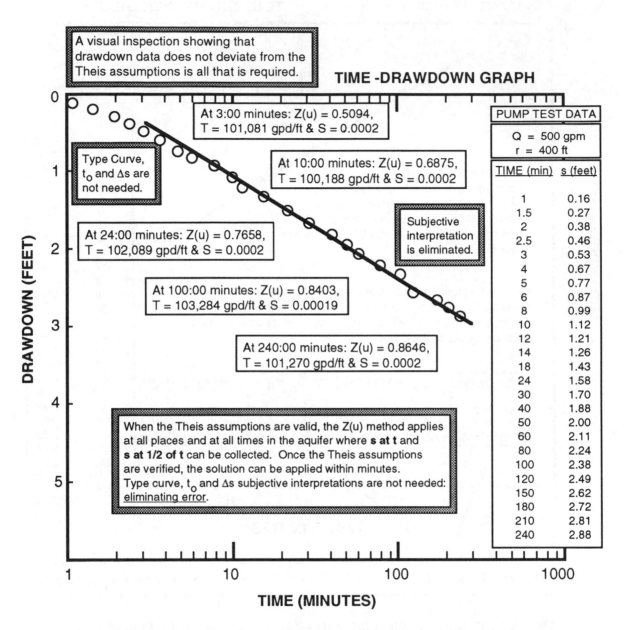

A visual inspection showing that drawdown data does not deviate from the Theis assumptions is all that is required.

TIME -DRAWDOWN GRAPH

At 3:00 minutes: Z(u) = 0.5094, T = 101,081 gpd/ft & S = 0.0002

Type Curve, t_o and Δs are not needed.

At 10:00 minutes: Z(u) = 0.6875, T = 100,188 gpd/ft & S = 0.0002

At 24:00 minutes: Z(u) = 0.7658, T = 102,089 gpd/ft & S = 0.0002

Subjective interpretation is eliminated.

At 100:00 minutes: Z(u) = 0.8403, T = 103,284 gpd/ft & S = 0.00019

At 240:00 minutes: Z(u) = 0.8646, T = 101,270 gpd/ft & S = 0.0002

When the Theis assumptions are valid, the Z(u) method applies at all places and at all times in the aquifer where **s at t** and **s at 1/2 of t** can be collected. Once the Theis assumptions are verified, the solution can be applied within minutes. Type curve, t_o and Δs subjective interpretations are not needed: <u>eliminating error</u>.

PUMP TEST DATA	
Q = 500 gpm	
r = 400 ft	
TIME (min)	s (feet)
1	0.16
1.5	0.27
2	0.38
2.5	0.46
3	0.53
4	0.67
5	0.77
6	0.87
8	0.99
10	1.12
12	1.21
14	1.26
18	1.43
24	1.58
30	1.70
40	1.88
50	2.00
60	2.11
80	2.24
100	2.38
120	2.49
150	2.62
180	2.72
210	2.81
240	2.88

DRAWDOWN (FEET)

TIME (MINUTES)

It would be foolish not to compare the Cooper- Jacob solution to the Z(u) solution, because the graph and apparent slope are already constructed: two solutions using the same graph can be compared (Figures 12 and 13). Yet it is important to understand that the Z(u) method is independent of the Theis type curve and Cooper - Jacob graphical methods.

FIGURE 11

SOLVING THE THEIS EQUATIONS WITHOUT THE THEIS CURVE: METHOD TWO-B

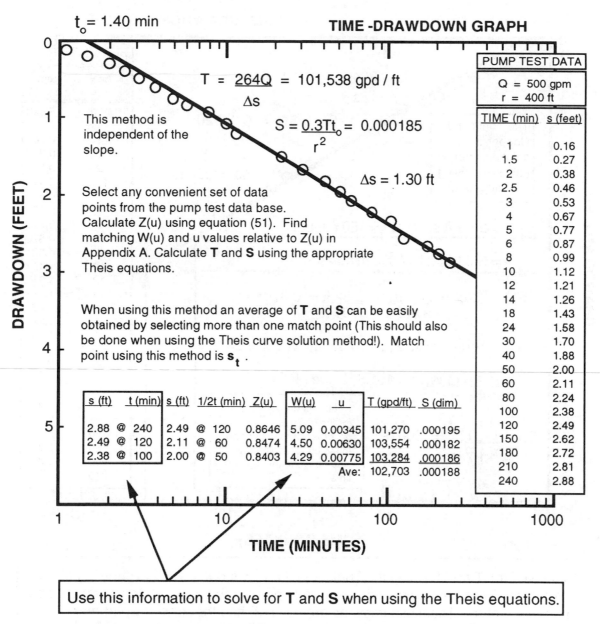

$t_o = 1.40$ min

TIME -DRAWDOWN GRAPH

$$T = \frac{264Q}{\Delta s} = 101{,}538 \text{ gpd / ft}$$

$$S = \frac{0.3Tt_o}{r^2} = 0.000185$$

$$\Delta s = 1.30 \text{ ft}$$

This method is independent of the slope.

Select any convenient set of data points from the pump test data base. Calculate Z(u) using equation (51). Find matching W(u) and u values relative to Z(u) in Appendix A. Calculate **T** and **S** using the appropriate Theis equations.

When using this method an average of **T** and **S** can be easily obtained by selecting more than one match point (This should also be done when using the Theis curve solution method!). Match point using this method is s_t.

PUMP TEST DATA

Q = 500 gpm
r = 400 ft

TIME (min)	s (feet)
1	0.16
1.5	0.27
2	0.38
2.5	0.46
3	0.53
4	0.67
5	0.77
6	0.87
8	0.99
10	1.12
12	1.21
14	1.26
18	1.43
24	1.58
30	1.70
40	1.88
50	2.00
60	2.11
80	2.24
100	2.38
120	2.49
150	2.62
180	2.72
210	2.81
240	2.88

s (ft)	t (min)	s (ft)	1/2t (min)	Z(u)	W(u)	u	T (gpd/ft)	S (dim)
2.88 @ 240		2.49 @ 120		0.8646	5.09	0.00345	101,270	.000195
2.49 @ 120		2.11 @ 60		0.8474	4.50	0.00630	103,554	.000182
2.38 @ 100		2.00 @ 50		0.8403	4.29	0.00775	103,284	.000186
						Ave:	102,703	.000188

DRAWDOWN (FEET)

TIME (MINUTES)

Use this information to solve for **T** and **S** when using the Theis equations.

The slope is constructed in order to validate the Theis assumptions. Drawdown is utilized as a match point.

One graph can be used with two solution methods. The results above are in reasonable agreement. Report the average values resulting from both the Theis and Cooper - Jacob solutions.

FIGURE 12

SOLVING THE THEIS EQUATIONS WITHOUT THE THEIS CURVE: METHOD TWO-C

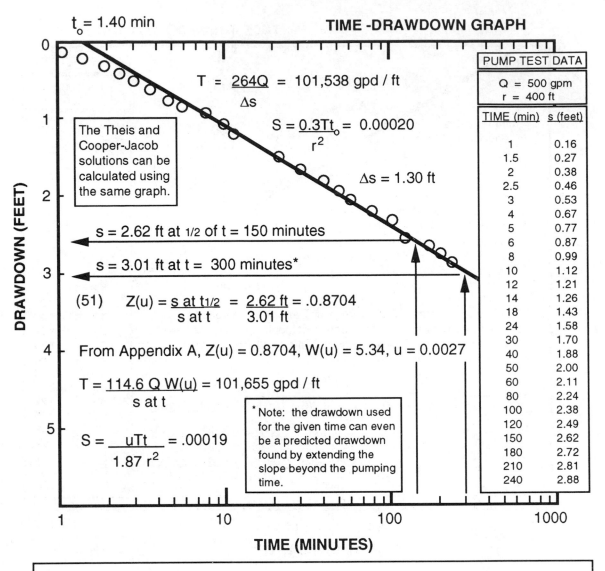

t_o = 1.40 min — TIME -DRAWDOWN GRAPH

$$T = \frac{264Q}{\Delta s} = 101,538 \text{ gpd} / \text{ft}$$

$$S = \frac{0.3Tt_o}{r^2} = 0.00020$$

$\Delta s = 1.30$ ft

The Theis and Cooper-Jacob solutions can be calculated using the same graph.

s = 2.62 ft at 1/2 of t = 150 minutes

s = 3.01 ft at t = 300 minutes*

(51) $Z(u) = \frac{s \text{ at } t_{1/2}}{s \text{ at } t} = \frac{2.62 \text{ ft}}{3.01 \text{ ft}} = .0.8704$

From Appendix A, Z(u) = 0.8704, W(u) = 5.34, u = 0.0027

$$T = \frac{114.6 \, Q \, W(u)}{s \text{ at } t} = 101,655 \text{ gpd} / \text{ft}$$

$$S = \frac{uTt}{1.87 \, r^2} = .00019$$

*Note: the drawdown used for the given time can even be a predicted drawdown found by extending the slope beyond the pumping time.

DRAWDOWN (FEET)

PUMP TEST DATA

Q = 500 gpm
r = 400 ft

TIME (min)	s (feet)
1	0.16
1.5	0.27
2	0.38
2.5	0.46
3	0.53
4	0.67
5	0.77
6	0.87
8	0.99
10	1.12
12	1.21
14	1.26
18	1.43
24	1.58
30	1.70
40	1.88
50	2.00
60	2.11
80	2.24
100	2.38
120	2.49
150	2.62
180	2.72
210	2.81
240	2.88

TIME (MINUTES)

To solve for **T** and **S** using the Theis equations without the Theis curve 1) plot the time-drawdown data points on semilogarithmic graph paper, 2) construct a slope to show that the Theis assumptions are valid, 3) find the drawdown at any convenient time **(s at t)** relative to the slope, 4) find the drawdown at half the time of t **(s at 1/2 of t)** relative to the slope, 5) use equation (51) to find Z(u), 6) find the matching W(u) and u values relative to Z(u) in Appendix A, 7) then use the appropriate Theis equations, depending upon units. The above results compare well to the Cooper - Jacob solution. Report the average of both solution methods.

FIGURE 13

SOLVING THE THEIS EQUATIONS WITHOUT
THE THEIS CURVE: BOUNDARY EFFECTS

The Z(u) solution can be used to estimate T and S before boundary conditions take effect. Use only time-drawdown data points that occur before the boundary effect.

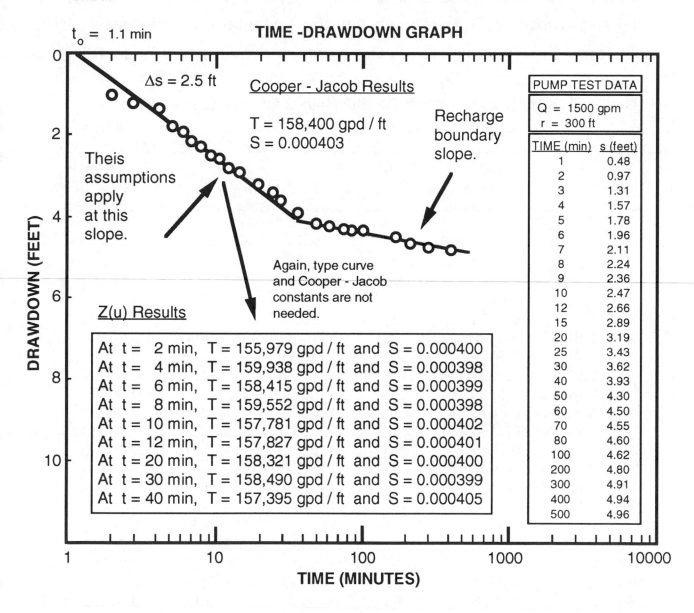

t_o = 1.1 min

TIME -DRAWDOWN GRAPH

Δs = 2.5 ft

Cooper - Jacob Results

T = 158,400 gpd / ft
S = 0.000403

Recharge boundary slope.

Theis assumptions apply at this slope.

Again, type curve and Cooper - Jacob constants are not needed.

Z(u) Results

At t = 2 min,	T = 155,979 gpd / ft	and S = 0.000400
At t = 4 min,	T = 159,938 gpd / ft	and S = 0.000398
At t = 6 min,	T = 158,415 gpd / ft	and S = 0.000399
At t = 8 min,	T = 159,552 gpd / ft	and S = 0.000398
At t = 10 min,	T = 157,781 gpd / ft	and S = 0.000402
At t = 12 min,	T = 157,827 gpd / ft	and S = 0.000401
At t = 20 min,	T = 158,321 gpd / ft	and S = 0.000400
At t = 30 min,	T = 158,490 gpd / ft	and S = 0.000399
At t = 40 min,	T = 157,395 gpd / ft	and S = 0.000405

DRAWDOWN (FEET)

TIME (MINUTES)

PUMP TEST DATA

Q = 1500 gpm
r = 300 ft

TIME (min)	s (feet)
1	0.48
2	0.97
3	1.31
4	1.57
5	1.78
6	1.96
7	2.11
8	2.24
9	2.36
10	2.47
12	2.66
15	2.89
20	3.19
25	3.43
30	3.62
40	3.93
50	4.30
60	4.50
70	4.55
80	4.60
100	4.62
200	4.80
300	4.91
400	4.94
500	4.96

In this example, only those points that occur at ≤ **40 minutes** should be used.

FIGURE 14

85

III) Another way in which the Z(u) method can replace the Theis type curve is to calculate T and S values for each drawdown at t and matching $t_{1/2}$. This is still often easier than constructing a logarithmic data curve and matching it to the Theis curve --- and it is more accurate. A series of aquifer parameters can then be listed in a table, the mean for T and S calculated, and results reported. This method has the advantage of offering a visual inspection of the distribution of aquifer parameters over time (Table 16).

TABLE 16: T and S calculated using the Z(u) method for all available points.
Source: Lohman (1972): r = 400 ft, Q = 500 gpm.

t min	s ft	Z(u)	W(u)	u	T gpd /ft	S
1	0.16	-----------	--------	-----------	-----------	-----------
1.5	0.27	-----------	--------	-----------	-----------	-----------
2	0.38	0.4211	0.640	0.44000	96,470	0.00020
2.5	0.46	-----------	--------	-----------	-----------	-----------
3	0.53	0.5094	0.935	0.29000	101,081	0.00020
4	0.67	0.5672	1.185	0.21000	101,384	0.00020
5	0.77	0.5974	1.342	0.17000	99,871	0.00020
6	0.87	0.6092	1.407	0.16000	92,692	0.00021
8	0.99	0.6768	1.871	0.09500	108,291	0.00019
10	1.12	0.6875	1.958	0.08600	100,188	0.00020
12	1.21	0.7190	2.249	0.06300	106,503	0.00019
24	1.58	0.7658	2.815	0.03500	102,089	0.00020
30	1.70	-----------	--------	-----------	-----------	-----------
40	1.88	-----------	--------	-----------	-----------	-----------
50	2.00	-----------	--------	-----------	-----------	-----------
60	2.11	0.8057	3.477	0.01800	94,415	0.00023
80	2.24	0.8393	4.262	0.00800	109,030	0.00016
100	2.38	0.8403	4.289	0.00780	103,264	0.00019
120	2.49	0.8474	4.496	0.00630	103,458	0.00018
240	2.88	0.8646	5.093	0.00350	101,330	0.00020
			Reported Mean:		101,433	0.00020
			Type Curve:		100,479	0.00020

It should be obvious that the Theis assumptions do not deviate a great deal relative to the values displayed in Table 16. Consistent values of T and S over time confirm the Theis assumptions (Figure 15). If T and S had changed dramatically over time, then a different method of analysis would have to be applied, such as, boundary or leaky confined solution methods (Figures 16 and 17).

Tables 17 and 18 offer comparisons between the Z(u) method and the Theis matching curve method using historical time-drawdown data. **Interpolation** was used to obtain the results displayed in Table 18, but a comparison between both tables reveals that interpolation is not necessary. The resulting comparisons appear to be very reasonable relative to historical data. The Z(u) method may be applicable as both a supplement and alternative to the Theis type curve and Cooper - Jacob graphical solutions.

When designing a pump test and to avoid interpolation, time - drawdown field data should be collected so that t is a consecutive multiple of 2, such as, 1, 2, 4, 8, 16, 32, 64, etc. This allows for a more efficient analysis when using the Z(u) method (Sheahan, 1967).

The Theis curve offers a **visual inspection** with its "fit" relative to the data points. If drawdown does not deviate from the Theis curve, then it is generally agreed that the Theis assumptions are valid. A **consistency** relative to "curve fitting" is required.

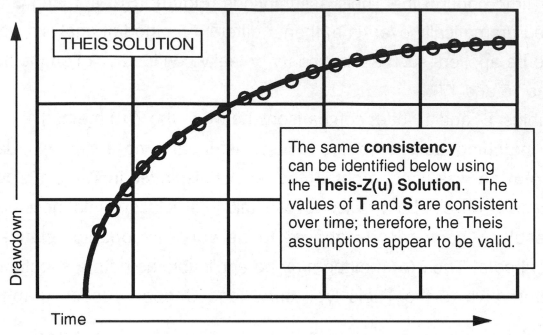

THEIS SOLUTION

Drawdown

The same **consistency** can be identified below using the **Theis-Z(u) Solution**. The values of **T** and **S** are consistent over time; therefore, the Theis assumptions appear to be valid.

Time

Theis Z(u) Solution

t min	s ft	Z(u)	u	W(u)	T gpd/ft	S
2	0.99	0.6667	1.0E-01	1.794	103842	0.000199
3	1.21	0.7190	6.3E-02	2.249	106503	0.000187
4	1.36	0.7279	5.7E-02	2.344	98742	0.000209
5	1.49	0.7450	4.6E-02	2.543	97784	0.000210
6	1.59	0.7610	3.7E-02	2.748	99042	0.000206
8	1.75	0.7771	2.9E-02	2.981	97615	0.000212
10	1.86	0.8011	1.9E-02	3.388	104375	0.000187
12	1.97	0.8071	1.7E-02	3.506	101962	0.000195
24	2.36	0.8347	9.0E-03	4.140	100530	0.000202
60	2.88	0.8646	3.5E-03	5.093	101330	0.000195
80	3.04	0.8717	2.6E-03	5.382	101452	0.000195
100	3.16	0.8797	1.8E-03	5.748	104232	0.000173
120	3.28	0.8780	1.9E-03	5.668	99010	0.000214
240	3.67	0.8937	8.4E-04	6.511	101562	0.000189
				Average ===>	101291	0.000198

FIGURE 15

COMPARISON BETWEEN THE Z(u) METHOD
AND THE THEIS CURVE MATCHING METHOD USING HISTORICAL DATA

TABLE 17 : Using only **drawdowns at t** that can be matched with **drawdowns at $t_{1/2}$: no interpolations**. Z(u) results in **bold**.

Source	T	S	T	S
Walton (1962)	10,100	.000020	**10,103**	**.000020**
Walton (1988)	35,082	.000390	**35,218**	**.000408**
Lohman (1972)	101,000*	.000200	**101,233**	**.000200**
Fetter (1988)	42,389	.000048	**40,225**	**.000050**
Heath & Trainer (1968)	115,000	.000200	**112,930**	**.000250**
Ground Water Manual (1981)$_1$	154,028*	.230000	**153,045***	**.250000**
Ground Water Manual (1981)$_2$	345,396*	.062000	**343,649****	**.066000**
Ground Water Manual (1981)$_3$	338,045	.063000	**339,594**	**.068700**
USGS WSP 1487 (1960)$_1$	17,200	.000070	**17,124**	**.000083**
USGS WSP 1487 (1960)$_2$	30,800*	.001130*	**31,173**	**.001300**
USGS WSP 1487 (1960)$_3$	16,120***	.000070***	**16,762**	**.000093**
Todd (1980)	89,355	.000206	**93,015**	**.000184**
Brown (1953)	50,000	.000200	**50,399**	**.000190**
Davis and DeWiest (1966)	20,500	.000315	**20,684**	**.000280**
Dawson and Istok (1991)	34,380	.000380	**34,297**	**.000383**

*Author's type curve results.   **Average of two observation wells.   ***Average of five observation wells.

Ground Water Manual 1 = p 96; 2 = p 108; 3 = p 119   USGS WSP 1487 1 = p 34; 2 = p 36; 3 = p 36

COMPARISON BETWEEN THE Z(u) METHOD
AND THE THEIS CURVE MATCHING METHOD USING HISTORICAL DATA

TABLE 18: Using **drawdowns at t** that can be matched with **drawdowns** at $t_{1/2}$ and **interpolation** of remaining drawdowns and times. Z(u) results in **bold**.

Source	T	S	T	S
Walton (1962)	10,100	.000020	**9,848**	**.000021**
Walton (1988)	35,082	.000390	**34,852**	**.000410**
Lohman (1972)	101,000*	.000200	**99,596**	**.000213**
Fetter (1988)	42,389	.000048	**40,011**	**.000053**
Heath & Trainer (1968)	115,000	.000200	**113,560**	**.000210**
Ground Water Manual (1981)$_1$	154,028*	.230000	**152,609***	**.250000**
Ground Water Manual (1981)$_2$	345,396*	.062000	**342,275***	**.065000**
Ground Water Manual (1981)$_3$	338,045	.063000	**330,000**	**.072000**
USGS WSP 1487 (1960)$_1$	17,200	.000070	**16,677**	**.000140**
USGS WSP 1487 (1960)$_2$	30,800*	.001130*	**30,839**	**.001200**
USGS WSP 1487 (1960)$_3$	16,120***	.000070***	**15,878**	**.000140**
Todd (1980)	89,355	.000206	**91,389**	**.000201**
Brown (1953)	50,000	.000200	**45,000**	**.000240**
Davis and DeWiest (1966)	20,500	.000315	**19,774**	**.000302**
Dawson and Istok (1991)	34,380	.000380	**34,387**	**.000380**

*Author's type curve results.   **Average of two observation wells.   ***Average of five observation wells.

Ground Water Manual 1 = p 96; 2 = p 108; 3 = p 119   USGS WSP 1487 1 = p 34; 2 = p 36; 3 = p 36

When drawdown deviates negatively (drawdown increases at a rate greater than expected) from the Theis curve, then it is generally agreed that the Theis assumptions are not valid. A barrier boundary is usually suspected.

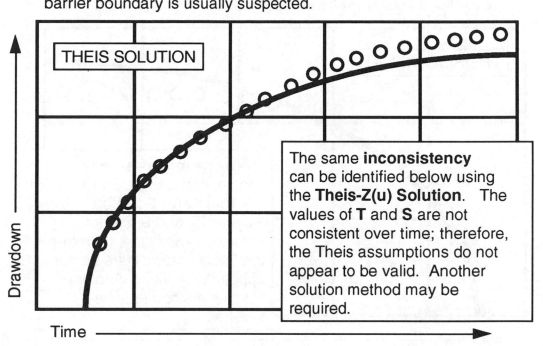

THEIS SOLUTION

The same **inconsistency** can be identified below using the **Theis-Z(u) Solution**. The values of **T** and **S** are not consistent over time; therefore, the Theis assumptions do not appear to be valid. Another solution method may be required.

Drawdown

Time

Theis Z(u) Solution

t min	s ft	Z(u)	u	W(u)	T gpd/ft	S
2	0.56	0.393	0.50	0.56	200000	.00742
4	1.07	0.523	0.27	0.99	185000	.00745
8	1.77	0.605	0.163	1.38	156000	.00755
16	2.70	0.656	0.115	1.70	126000	.00863
32	3.81	0.709	0.069	2.18	114000	.00935
64	5.00	0.762	0.038	2.75	110000	.00995
128	6.31	0.792	0.0225	3.25	103000	.01100
256	7.66	0.824	0.0116	3.90	102000	.01125
512	9.02	0.849	0.0060	4.55	101000	.01150

Average ===>   133000   0.00934

*Transmissivity is **decreasing over time**, which may indicate the presence of a barrier boundary. Another solution method may be required.*

FIGURE 16

91

When drawdown deviates positively (drawdown decreases at a rate greater than expected) from the Theis curve, then it is generally agreed that the Theis assumptions are not valid. A leaky confined aquifer is often suspected.

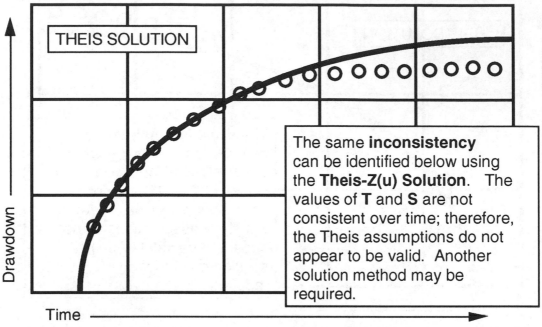

THEIS SOLUTION

Drawdown

Time

The same **inconsistency** can be identified below using the **Theis-Z(u) Solution**. The values of **T** and **S** are not consistent over time; therefore, the Theis assumptions do not appear to be valid. Another solution method may be required.

Theis Z(u) Solution

t min	s ft	Z(u)	u	W(u)	T gpd/ft	S
2	2.15	0.4186	4.4E-01	0.633	18885	0.000928
4	3.64	0.5907	1.8E-01	1.306	23033	0.000920
6	4.52	0.6748	9.7E-02	1.853	26315	0.000843
8	5.02	0.7251	5.9E-02	2.314	29583	0.000769
10	5.53	0.7360	5.2E-02	2.430	28201	0.000810
20	5.97	0.9263	4.6E-05	9.404	101091	0.000005
30	6.12	0.9346	1.4E-05	10.603	111188	0.000003
40	6.20	0.9629	4.3E-09	18.685	193406	0.000000
60	6.27	0.9700	5.4E-11	23.072	<u>236151</u>	<u>0.000000</u>

Average ===> 85317   0.000475

*Transmissivity is **increasing over time**, which may indicate that the aquifer is leaky confined. Another solution method may be required.*

FIGURE 17

92

THEIS: DISTANCE-DRAWDOWN SOLUTION

IV) Similar to method (II) for time-drawdown, **Z(u) can be used to simplify the Theis distance-drawdown solution**. Again, look for consistency in the results. This method can also be used with a semilog graph (Figure 18), and as before, it offers two solutions using the same graph --- which can be compared. Again, Z(u) has the advantage that it can be used for early drawdown data (Tables 21 and 22).

Z(u) -- Distance Drawdown Example: Without Graphs

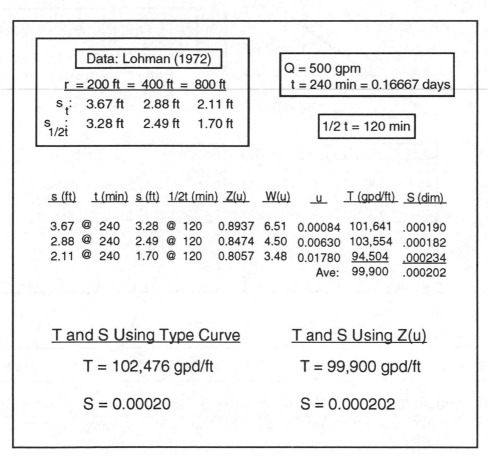

Data: Lohman (1972)	Q = 500 gpm
r = 200 ft = 400 ft = 800 ft	t = 240 min = 0.16667 days
s_t: 3.67 ft 2.88 ft 2.11 ft	
$s_{1/2t}$: 3.28 ft 2.49 ft 1.70 ft	1/2 t = 120 min

s (ft)	t (min)	s (ft)	1/2t (min)	Z(u)	W(u)	u	T (gpd/ft)	S (dim)
3.67 @	240	3.28 @	120	0.8937	6.51	0.00084	101,641	.000190
2.88 @	240	2.49 @	120	0.8474	4.50	0.00630	103,554	.000182
2.11 @	240	1.70 @	120	0.8057	3.48	0.01780	94,504	.000234
						Ave:	99,900	.000202

T and S Using Type Curve	T and S Using Z(u)
T = 102,476 gpd/ft	T = 99,900 gpd/ft
S = 0.00020	S = 0.000202

Distance-drawdown Theis curve results reported above are from Lohman (1972) who used the Theis curve method for distance-drawdown, not time-drawdown.

SOLVING THE THEIS EQUATIONS WITHOUT
THE THEIS CURVE: DISTANCE - DRAWDOWN METHOD

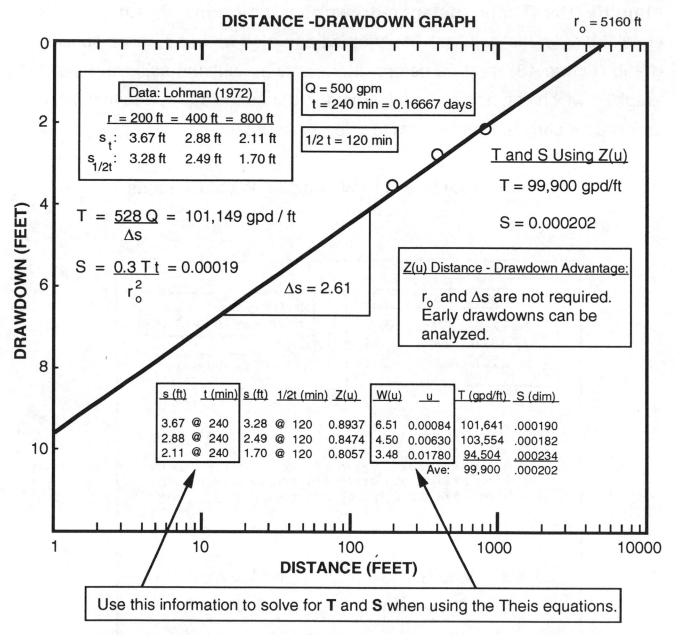

DISTANCE -DRAWDOWN GRAPH

$r_o = 5160$ ft

Data: Lohman (1972)

r =	200 ft	= 400 ft	= 800 ft
s_t:	3.67 ft	2.88 ft	2.11 ft
$s_{1/2t}$:	3.28 ft	2.49 ft	1.70 ft

Q = 500 gpm
t = 240 min = 0.16667 days

1/2 t = 120 min

$$T = \frac{528\,Q}{\Delta s} = 101,149 \text{ gpd / ft}$$

$$S = \frac{0.3\,T\,t}{r_o^2} = 0.00019$$

$\Delta s = 2.61$

T and S Using Z(u)

T = 99,900 gpd/ft

S = 0.000202

Z(u) Distance - Drawdown Advantage:

r_o and Δs are not required. Early drawdowns can be analyzed.

s (ft)	t (min)	s (ft)	1/2t (min)	Z(u)	W(u)	u	T (gpd/ft)	S (dim)
3.67	@ 240	3.28	@ 120	0.8937	6.51	0.00084	101,641	.000190
2.88	@ 240	2.49	@ 120	0.8474	4.50	0.00630	103,554	.000182
2.11	@ 240	1.70	@ 120	0.8057	3.48	0.01780	94,504	.000234
						Ave:	99,900	.000202

DRAWDOWN (FEET)

DISTANCE (FEET)

Use this information to solve for **T** and **S** when using the Theis equations.

Find Z(u) and matching u and W(u) for each drawdown relative to distance. Use the Theis equations to solve for T and S. Compute the average values.

FIGURE 18

COMPARISON BETWEEN THE Z(u) METHOD
AND THE THEIS MATCHING CURVE METHOD USING HISTORICAL DATA:
DISTANCE-DRAWDOWN

TABLE 19: Distance-drawdown comparisons: Theis Curve vs Z(u) (in **bold**).
t = 240 minutes for both examples.

Source	T (gpd / ft)	S	T (gpd / ft)	S
Lohman (1972)	102,476	.000200	**99,900**	**.000202**
Ground Water Manual (1981)	150,904	.240000	**150,696**	**.250000**

TABLE 20: Distance-drawdown comparisons for **most of the available times**.
Z(u) results in **bold**. r = 200, 400 and 800 ft; Q = 500 gpm.

Source	t (min)	T (gpd / ft)	S	T (gpd / ft)	S
Lohman (1972)	240	102,476	.000200	**99,900**	**.000202**
(Theis Curve)	120	N/A	N/A	**100,871**	**.000200**
	100	N/A	N/A	**101,291**	**.000190**
	80	N/A	N/A	**103,821**	**.000185**
	60	N/A	N/A	**97,902**	**.000213**
	24	N/A	N/A	**98,437**	**.000202**
	12	N/A	N/A	**103,182**	**.000195**
	10	N/A	N/A	**102,259**	**.000196**
	8	N/A	N/A	**103,366**	**.000202**
	6	N/A	N/A	**91,804**	**.000202**
	5	N/A	N/A	**101,223**	**.000203**

TABLE 21: Distance-drawdown comparisons for **most of the available times**. Z(u) results in **bold**. r = 200, 400 and 800 ft; Q = 500 gpm. Source T = 102,476 gpd / ft and S = .000200.

Source	t (min)	T (gpd / ft)	S	**T (gpd / ft)**	**S**
Lohman (1972)	240	101,538	.000200	**99,900**	**.000202**
(Cooper-Jacob)	120	100,542	.000200	**100,871**	**.000200**
	100	103,154	.000183	**101,291**	**.000190**
	80	102,488	.000188	**103,821**	**.000185**
	60	101,831	.000189	**97,902**	**.000213**
	24	106,615	.000169	**98,437**	**.000202**
	12	110,317	.000160	**103,182**	**.000195**
	10	113,469	.000153	**102,259**	**.000196**
	8	115,114	.000150	**103,366**	**.000202**
	6	120,346	.000140	**91,804**	**.000202**
	5	125,084	.000134	**101,223**	**.000203**

Table 21 compares the Z(u) method to the Cooper-Jacob solution. Z(u) results are more consistent relative to early distance-drawdown times. The values above should range around 101,000 gpd/ft for T and about .00020 for S. At 24 minutes the Cooper-Jacob method begins to exaggerate transmissivity and underestimate the storage coefficient. This, of course, is consistent with the limitations of the semilog methods as expressed by Cooper and Jacob (1946).

TABLE 22: Distance-drawdown comparisons for **most of the available times**. Z(u) results in **bold**. r = 30, 60 and 120 ft; Q = 1166.9 gpm. Source T = 150,904 gpd / ft and S = 0.24.

Source	t (min)	T (gpd / ft)	S	**T (gpd / ft)**	**S**
Ground Water	240	164,791	0.198000	**150,696**	**.250000**
Manual (1981)	180	169,288	0.190000	**150,907**	**.248000**
(Cooper-Jacob)	120	179,971	0.175000	**153,031**	**.250000**
	100	184,448	0.170000	**146,628**	**.251000**
	90	188,193	0.166000	**153,502**	**.255000**

Table 22 offers more evidence relative to the consistency and accuracy of the Z(u) distance-drawdown method. T values should be around 150,000 gpd/ft and S values around 0.24, according to the source. Again, Cooper-Jacob exaggerates transmissivity and underestimates the storage coefficient. Z(u) appears to be accurate.

THE DELAYED YIELD PROBLEM

The $Z(u)$ method can be used to estimate **T** and **S$_y$** when analyzing water table aquifers that have a delayed yield, especially when very late drawdowns are analyzed. Simply analyze **late s_t values** that have corresponding **$s_{1/2t}$ values** using the methods described above. Obtain average parameter values when the appropriate drawdowns are available. The $Z(u)$ method is not always applicable for analyzing delayed yield aquifer parameters using early drawdown data, especially when t < 5.0 minutes (Table 23).

COMPARISON BETWEEN THE Z(u) - THEIS METHOD
AND DELAYED YIELD MATCHING CURVE METHODS USING HISTORICAL DATA

TABLE 23: Unconfined delayed yield comparisons. $Z(u)$ results in **bold**.

Source	T	S	**T**	**S**
Fairborn, OH (Lohman 1972)				
Early drawdown results	299,200	0.00300	**295,350**	**0.00290**
Late drawdown results	261,800	0.10000	**265,670**	**0.10000**
Lawrenceville, Ill, (Walton 1988)				
Early drawdown results	266,511	0.03160	**N/A**	**N/A**
Late drawdown results	260,454	0.03400	**263,524**	**0.02500**

Advantages and Uses of the Z(u) Method

1) The Z(u) method is easy to apply.

2) A type curve is not needed; **the error of subjective interpretation is eliminated.**

3) Time-drawdown solutions require only two drawdowns: s_t and $s_{1/2t}$.

4) Because only two drawdowns are required, **T and S can be easily calculated in the field**, and at any time after pumping begins.

5) A visual inspection of T and S can be observed over time.

6) A solution can be obtained without graphical analysis --or-- the method can be set up on a time-drawdown, semilog graph, but Δs and t_o do not need to be constructed or identified. **This again removes the error of subjective interpretation**. A visual inspection that shows the data points do not deviate from a straight line on the time-drawdown graph is all that is needed to validate the Theis assumptions. Δs and t_o are not needed in the calculations.

7) Yet it would be foolish not to compare the Z(u) method to a semilog, time-drawdown method. Two solutions on one graph can be obtained and the results reported with confidence: Theis and Cooper-Jacob.

8) Method can use a predicted drawdown for s_t.

9) Method can be applied to late drawdown, delayed yield data.

10) Method can be applied to boundary conditions.

11) Method can be applied to distance-drawdown calculations.

12) Method can be used to evaluate early drawdown data.

13) A view of a series of time vs drawdowns can help to identify values of T and S that change significantly from average values. By simply reviewing the significant changes in T and S, boundary and leaky confined conditions can be inferred.

14) Other conditions may be easily identified by simply reviewing the changes in T and S: heterogeneities, aquifer thickness, permeability, etc.

SIX

ESTIMATING TRANSMISSIVITY
FROM STEP-DRAWDOWN TESTS

WELL LOSS COEFFICIENT

The well loss coefficient **(C)** is often used to approximate well loss and well efficiency when observation wells are not available. **Significant error may result when using this method.** Jacob (1947) suggested that the total drawdown **(s)** in the pumping well could be expressed as the sum of the drawdown component due to laminar flow **(s_a)** and the drawdown component due to pumping well turbulence **(s_w)**:

$$s = s_a + s_w \qquad (52)$$

where

$$s_a = BQ = \text{well loss due to laminar flow,} \qquad (53)$$
$$= \text{the drawdown in the aquifer,}$$
$$= \text{the theoretical drawdown,}$$
$$= \text{the expected drawdown in the pumping well,}$$

$$B = \text{laminar flow well loss coefficient,}$$

$$s_w = CQ^2 = \text{well loss due to turbulent flow,} \qquad (54)$$

$$C = \text{turbulent flow well loss coefficient,}$$
$$= \text{well loss coefficient}$$

and

$$s = BQ + CQ^2 . \qquad (55)$$

Jacob assumed that the terms BQ and CQ^2 were exclusive of each other. That assumption is no longer considered to be valid (Driscoll 1986); therefore, **the well loss (s_w) as a product of the well loss coefficient**

should not be used in isolation to determine well efficiency. Well loss as a product of the well loss coefficient describes well loss resulting from pumping well turbulence. It does not describe that part of well loss resulting from laminar flow.

THEORETICAL WELL LOSS COMPONENTS

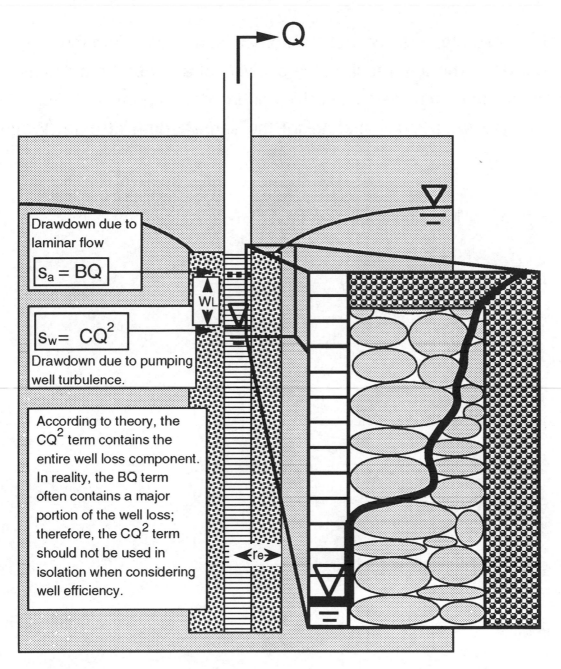

A gravel pack, which is much more permeable relative to the natural sedimentary material, increases velocity of groundwater as it enters the effective radius (r_e).

FIGURE 19

STEP DRAWDOWN TEST: METHOD ONE

Data from a step-drawdown test is often used to calculate the well loss coefficient **(C)**. The test requires the analysis of at least three production well drawdowns from three successive and increased pumping rates. The three pumping rates must operate for the same length of time (Walton, 1962).

C_x = the well loss coefficient = sec^2 / ft^5

$$C_1 = \frac{(\Delta s_2 / \Delta Q_2) - (\Delta s_1 / \Delta Q_1)}{\Delta Q_1 + \Delta Q_2} \qquad (56)$$

and

$$C_2 = \frac{(\Delta s_3 / \Delta Q_3) - (\Delta s_2 / \Delta Q_2)}{\Delta Q_2 + \Delta Q_3} \qquad (57)$$

$$C_3 = C_1 + C_2 / 2 \qquad (58)$$

where   Q = cubic feet / sec

and   1 cfs = 449 gpm. $\qquad\qquad$ (59)

The above method is appropriate for step tests with three variable rates. If the well is stable C_1 should approximate C_2. If C_1 does not approximate C_2 or if the number of variable rates exceeds three another method should be used.

STEP-DRAWDOWN TEST: EXAMPLE

The data collected from a step-drawdown test is listed below:

After one hour of pumping at $Q_1 = 500$ gpm , $s_1 = 5.55$ ft.

In the second hour of pumping $Q_2 = 800$ gpm and $s_2 = 8.99$ ft.

In the third hour of pumping $Q_3 = 1000$ gpm and $s_3 = 11.5$ ft.

1) <u>Compile the data into a table</u>:   1cfs = 449 gpm

Step	Q(gpm)	ΔQ(gpm)	ΔQ(cfs)	s(ft)	Δs(ft)
1	500	500	1.114	5.55	5.55
2	800	300	0.668	8.99	3.44
3	1000	200	0.445	11.5	2.51

2) <u>Calculate C_1 using equation (56)</u>

$$C_1 = \frac{(\Delta s_2 / \Delta Q_2) - (\Delta s_1 / \Delta Q_1)}{\Delta Q_1 + \Delta Q_2} = \frac{(3.44 / 0.668) - (5.55 / 1.114)}{(1.114) + (0.668)}$$

$$C_1 = 0.094 \text{ sec}^2 / \text{ft}^5$$

3) <u>Calculate C_2 using equation (57)</u>

$$C_2 = \frac{(\Delta s_3 / \Delta Q_3) - (\Delta s_2 / \Delta Q_2)}{\Delta Q_2 + \Delta Q_3} = \frac{(2.51 / 0.445) - (3.44 / 0.668)}{(0.668) + (0.445)}$$

$$C_2 = 0.441 \text{ sec}^2 / \text{ft}^5$$

4) <u>Calculate C_3 using equation (58)</u>

$$C_3 = C_1 + C_2 / 2 = (0.094) + (0.441) / 2 = 0.267 \text{ sec}^2 / \text{ft}^5$$

5) *What is the well loss due to turbulence in the pumping well when the total drawdown in the pumping well is 12.5 feet at Q = 1000 gpm?*

<u>Use equation (54)</u>

$$s_w = CQ^2 = (0.267 \text{ sec}^2 / \text{ft}^5)(1000 \text{ gpm} / 449)^2 = 1.32 \text{ ft}$$

OR 1.32 ft / 12.5 ft x 100 = 10.6% of the drawdown in the pumping well. This component of drawdown is generally produced by well turbulence.

ALTERNATIVE STEP-DRAWDOWN TEST:
MULTIPLE PUMPING RATES

Bierschenk (1963) developed an alternative step-drawdown test utilizing multiple pumping rates at equal times and an arithmetic graph. Rearranging equation (55) results in

$$s/Q = CQ + B, \tag{60}$$

which is a linear equation. Plotting s/Q against Q results in a straight-line slope with C = slope and B = y-intercept. Inverting equation (60) produces an equation that can predict specific capacity for any discharge rate (Q) once C and B have been defined:

$$Q/s = 1/(CQ + B). \tag{61}$$

The data below, original to Bierschenk's paper, will be used to demonstrate this method:

Step	Q gpm	s feet	s/Q
1	100	2.5	0.0250
2	200	6.5	0.0325
3	400	22.2	0.0555
4	500	34.9	0.0696
5	550	46.5	0.0845

After compiling the above data construct an arithmetic graph, plot the data, and find C (slope) and B (y-intercept):

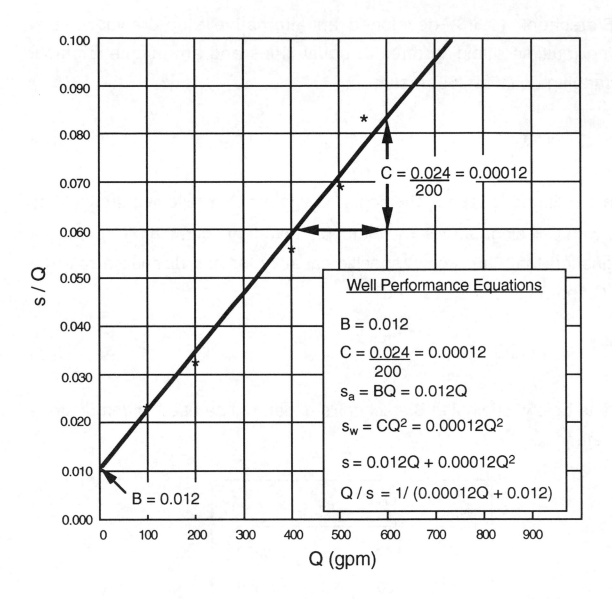

Well Performance Equations

B = 0.012

$$C = \frac{0.024}{200} = 0.00012$$

$s_a = BQ = 0.012Q$

$s_w = CQ^2 = 0.00012Q^2$

$s = 0.012Q + 0.00012Q^2$

$Q/s = 1/(0.00012Q + 0.012)$

FIGURE 20

Specific capacity (Q / s) and production well drawdown can now be predicted for any flow rate (Q) using the well performance equations.

Regression analysis can be applied to Bierschenk's step-drawdown method, and it probably increases accuracy, because it eliminates human error relative to the construction of the slope and y-intercept. The slope (C) and the y-intercept (B) can be defined by the following equations:

$$C = \frac{n\Sigma xy - (\Sigma x)(\Sigma y)}{n\Sigma x^2 - (\Sigma x)^2} \qquad (62)$$

$$B = \frac{(\Sigma y)(\Sigma x^2) - (\Sigma x)(\Sigma xy)}{n\Sigma x^2 - (\Sigma x)^2} \qquad (63)$$

where,

n = steps

x = the pumping rate at a particular step = gpm,

y = s / Q, and

xy = s

In addition to being more accurate relative to the graphical method, the regression analysis method is probably the easiest to use. A graph does not need to be constructed and the same data is utilized with one additional column included. To solve for C and B using regression analysis, set up a table similar to the one used with the graphical method, but add a column for x^2 (which is Q^2), sum up the results, and plug into equations (62) and (63). Again, Bierschenk's data will be used to demonstrate this method:

n	x	x²	y	xy
	Q		$\frac{s}{Q}$	s
Step	gpm	Q²		feet
1	100	10000	0.0250	2.5
2	200	40000	0.0325	6.5
3	400	160000	0.0555	22.2
4	500	250000	0.0696	34.9
5	550	302500	0.0845	46.5
Σ = 5	1750	762500	0.2671	112.6

$(\Sigma x)^2 = (1750 \times 1750) = 3062500$

$$C = \frac{5(112.6) - (1750)(0.2671)}{5(762500) - (3062500)} = 0.000127$$

$$B = \frac{(0.2671)(762500) - (1750)(112.6)}{5(762500) - (3062500)} = 0.0088$$

The well performance equations can then be defined:

$B = 0.0088$

$C = 0.000127$

$s_a = BQ = 0.0088Q$

$s_w = CQ^2 = 0.000127Q^2$

$s = 0.0088Q + 0.000127Q^2$

$Q/s = 1/(0.000127Q + 0.0088)$

Transmissivity can be easily estimated from a step-drawdown test using the Z(u) method when the Theis assumptions are working. Calculate Z(u) values for drawdowns collected during the interval of the first step using equation (51). Find matching W(u) and u values in Appendix A. Depending upon units, use the Theis equations to calculate all possible transmissivities, then calculate an average value. The procedure is demonstrated below.

Pump test observation well data have been collected for a confined aquifer. The follow constants and variables were used to calculate the following parameters:

$Q = 200$ gpm,

$r_1 = 50$ ft, $r_2 = 200$ ft, $r_3 = 500$ ft,

$b = 90$ ft,

$t = 500$ minutes

$T = 45,451$ gpd/ft (average)

$K = 505$ gpd/ft^2 (average)

$S = 0.0004$ (average)

A step-drawdown test was completed using the production well, which has a well radius of .5 ft.

Time-drawdown data for the observation well and step-drawdown data for the production well are on pages 114 and 115. A good match is anticipated between transmissivity calculated using observation well data and transmissivity using step-drawdown data if the Theis assumptions are satisfied.

Confined Observation Well Data: Q = 200 gpm

t (min)	r₁ = 50 ft	r₂ = 200 ft	r₃ = 500 ft
2.00	1.50	0.30	0.01
2.50	1.61	0.37	0.01
5.00	1.95	0.64	0.08
10.00	2.30	0.94	0.23
15.00	2.50	1.13	0.36
20.00	2.64	1.27	0.46
25.00	2.76	1.38	0.55
35.00	2.93	1.54	0.69
40.00	2.99	1.61	0.74
50.00	3.11	1.72	0.84
60.00	3.20	1.81	0.92
70.00	3.28	1.88	1.00
80.00	3.34	1.95	1.06
90.00	3.40	2.01	1.11
100.00	3.45	2.06	1.16
120.00	3.55	2.15	1.25
150.00	3.66	2.26	1.36
200.00	3.80	2.41	1.50
250.00	3.92	2.52	1.61
300.00	4.01	2.61	1.70
400.00	4.15	2.76	1.84
500.00	4.27	2.87	1.95

T =	45,554	45,473	45,326 gpd/ft
S =	0.0004	0.0004	0.0004

114

Step-Drawdown Data for the Production Well

1st Step Q = 75 gpm		2nd Step Q = 200 gpm, t = 120 min
t (min)	s (ft)	s = 9.20
10	2.66	3rd Step Q = 500 gpm, t = 120 min
15	2.74	
20	2.79	s = 25.37
25	2.83	
35	2.90	4th Step Q = 800 gpm, t = 120 min
40	2.92	
50	2.97	s = 41.08
60	3.00	
70	3.03	5th Step Q = 1000 gpm, t = 120 min
80	3.05	
90	3.08	s = 51.55
100	3.10	
120	3.13	

Confined Aquifer Step Drawdown Example Results

Bierschenk's method was used to calculate the laminar flow well loss and the turbulent flow well loss coefficients:

B = laminar flow well loss coefficient = 0.043.
C = turbulent flow well loss coefficient = 0.00000988.

Drawdown in the aquifer (s_a) and drawdown in the production well (s_w) were then calculated for the first step Q value of 75 gpm:

$s_a = BQ = 3.24$ ft.
$s_w = CQ^2 = 0.0556$ ft.

The theoretical drawdown in the production well was then totaled:

$s_t = BQ + CQ^2 = 3.29$ ft.

The above value does not include drawdown due to entrance velocity. The theoretical specific capacity was then calculated:

$Q / s = 1 / (CQ + B) = 22.77$ gpm / ft.

The correlation coefficient was determined to be R = 0.895.

Transmissivity was then calculated for every s_t value that has a corresponding $s_{1/2t}$ value using Z(u) equation (51), Appendix A, and the correct Theis equations. Resulting transmissivities are listed below.

Drawdown (ft)	Transmissivity (gpd/ft)
S at t = 20 minutes	45,828
S at t = 40 minutes	45,828
S at t = 50 minutes	42,554
S at t = 70 minutes	45,793
S at t = 80 minutes	45,784
S at t = 100 minutes	45,828
S at t = 120 minutes	<u>45,828</u>
Reported mean =	45,349

Transmissivity calculated for the production well using drawdown values from the first step interval and the Z(u) method are in reasonable agreement with T values calculated using observation well pump test data. Drawdowns from the step test used to calculate T values were adjusted for well loss, but this is often not necessary when using drawdowns from the first interval, because well loss drawdown is considered to be a constant for a specific value. Subtracting a constant from all of the drawdowns results in a refinement of T values. Simply put --- if the Theis assumptions are working, and unless well loss is extreme, T values before and after correction for well loss will --- using the first step interval --- be approximately equal. The described method offers an alternative to observation well pump test evaluation, when the Theis assumptions are working, especially when cost is a major consideration.

The well loss ($s_w = CQ^2 = 0.0556$ ft) was negligible for the relatively low pumping well discharge of 75 gpm. The low discharge rate is a good reason for using drawdown data from the first interval to calculate transmissivity when using this method, but a low pumping rate does not stress the aquifer system; therefore, erroneous T values are possible. Well loss increases with increasing pumping rate. When predicting well loss ($s_w = CQ^2$) for Q values at 300, 500, 750 and 1000 gpm, it is easy to understand the importance of knowing this parameter:

<u>Predicted well loss values</u>

Q = 300 gpm	$s_w = CQ^2 = 0.89$ ft
Q = 500 gpm	$s_w = CQ^2 = 2.47$ ft
Q = 750 gpm	$s_w = CQ^2 = 5.56$ ft
Q = 1000 gpm	$s_w = CQ^2 = 9.88$ ft

If a reasonable consistency of T values does not occur when using this method, then an alternative method should be used to estimate T values from step-drawdown data.

GROUNDWATER FLOW TOWARD A PRODUCTION WELL

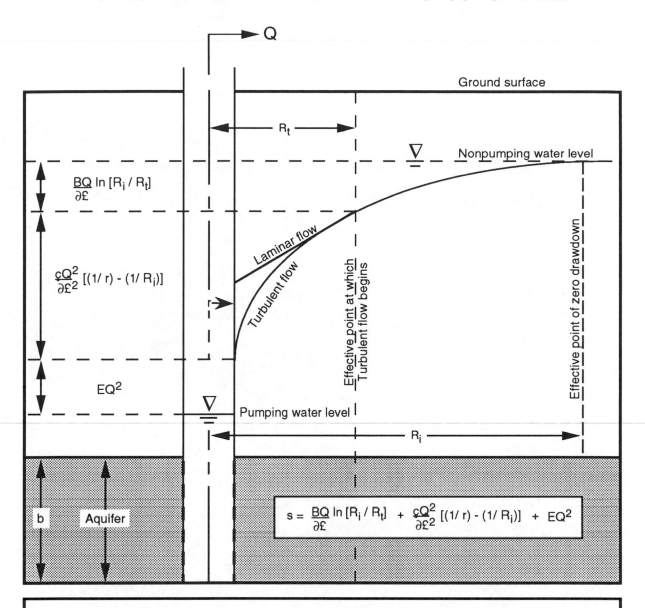

$$s = \frac{BQ}{\partial \pounds} \ln [R_i / R_t] + \frac{\text{ç}Q^2}{\partial \pounds^2} [(1/r) - (1/R_i)] + EQ^2$$

s = drawdown in the production well
Q = pumping rate
B = $K\mu^2 g$
∂ = $D^2 P$
$\pounds$ = $2\pi bP$
ç = $K_1 D2g$
R_i = extent of the cone of depression
r = radius of production well
R_t = distance where transition from laminar to turbulent flow takes place

K = laminar flow coefficient of aquifer
K_1 = turbulent flow coefficient of formation
g = gravitational constant
μ = viscosity of water in the aquifer
D = length parameter used in Reynold's number, probably representative of the pore size in the aquifer.
P = density of water in the aquifer
b = effective thickness of aquifer
P = effective permeability of aquifer
E = a coefficient to account for entrance loss into the well and the turbulent flow of water within the well.

Modified from Bruin and Hudson (1955).

FIGURE 21

SEVEN

KASENOW'S METHOD

KASENOW'S METHOD

The Theis equation can be manipulated to solve for specific capacity:

for consistent units,
$$Q/s = T4\pi / W(u). \tag{64}$$

In order to use equation (64), u must first be defined so that W(u) can be obtained from Appendix A:

for consistent units,
$$u = Sr^2 / 4Tt. \tag{2}$$

where

Q = production well discharge

T = transmissivity,

S = the storage coefficient,

r = production well radius,

t = time duration of pump test,

s = drawdown, and

Q/s = the specific capacity.

The storage coefficient is often estimated in order to work equation (2).

Kasenow (1993), observing Patchick's tables (1967), realized that equations (2) and (64) could be solved simultaneously in a spreadsheet format, using a computer, and that T could be interpolated from the two values between which the calculated Q/s was situated.

Table 24. Theoretical Specific Capacities Calculated from Theoretical Transmissivities

Assumed Confined Conditions S = .0005								
Small Diameter Wells (e.g. d = diameter = 6 inch)				**Large Diameter Wells** (e.g. d = diameter = 12 inch)				
T gpd/ft	**Pumping Period (days)**			**T** gpd/ft	**Pumping Period (days)**			
	.5	1.0	10		.5	1.0	10	
1,000	0.6	0.5	0.5	1,000	0.6	0.6	0.5	
2,000	1.1	1.0	0.9	2,000	1.2	1.1	1.0	
3,000	1.6	1.5	1.3	3,000	1.7	1.7	1.5	
4,000	2.1	2.0	1.8	4,000	2.3	2.2	2.0	**Q**
5,000	2.6	2.5	2.2	5,000	2.8	2.7	2.4	**S**
10,000	4.9	4.6	4.2	10,000	5.4	5.1	4.5	
15,000	7.2	7.0	6.2	15,000	7.9	7.5	6.7	
20,000	9.5	9.2	8.2	20,000	10.3	9.9	8.8	
30,000	13.9	13.4	12.0	30,000	15.1	14.5	12.8	
40,000	18.3	17.6	15.8	40,000	19.8	19.0	16.9	**gpm**
50,000	22.6	21.9	19.6	50,000	24.3	23.5	21.0	**ft**
60,000	25.9	26.0	23.3	60,000	29.0	27.9	24.8	
70,000	31.1	30.1	27.0	70,000	33.4	32.3	28.7	
80,000	35.4	34.1	30.7	80,000	38.0	36.6	32.7	
100,000	43.6	42.1	38.0	100,000	46.8	45.1	40.3	
125,000	53.8	52.2	47.0	125,000	57.0	56.0	50.0	
150,000	64.4	62.1	56.0	150,000	69.0	66.5	59.6	
175,000	73.7	71.8	65.0	175,000	79.6	76.9	68.9	
200,000	84.3	81.8	73.7	200,000	90.7	87.5	78.5	

After Patchick (1967)

124

Table 25. Theoretical Specific Capacities
Calculated from Theoretical Transmissivities

Assumed Water table Conditions $S_y = .1$							
Small Diameter Wells (e.g. d = diameter = 6 inch)				Large Diameter Wells (e.g. d = diameter = 12 inch)			
T gpd/ft	Pumping Period (days) .5	1.0	10	T gpd/ft	Pumping Period (days) .5	1.0	10
1,000	0.9	0.8	0.7	1,000	1.0	0.9	0.8
2,000	1.6	1.5	1.3	2,000	1.7	1.7	1.4
3,000	2.3	2.2	1.9	3,000	2.6	2.5	2.1
4,000	3.0	2.9	2.4	4,000	3.5	3.3	2.7
5,000	3.7	3.5	3.0	5,000	4.2	4.0	3.3
10,000	7.0	7.0	6.0	10,000	7.9	7.5	6.2
15,000	10.3	9.7	8.3	15,000	11.5	10.8	9.1
20,000	13.3	12.6	10.8	20,000	14.9	14.0	11.8
30,000	19.4	18.4	15.9	30,000	21.6	20.5	17.4
40,000	25.4	24.0	20.8	40,000	28.1	26.7	22.7
50,000	31.1	29.5	25.5	50,000	34.6	32.6	27.9
60,000	37.1	35.0	30.4	60,000	40.9	38.8	33.1
70,000	42.6	40.6	35.2	70,000	47.0	44.2	38.4
80,000	48.2	46.0	39.8	80,000	53.5	50.6	44.4
100,000	59.3	56.7	49.4	100,000	65.3	62.2	53.4
125,000	73.2	69.8	60.8	125,000	80.2	76.5	65.8
150,000	86.7	82.8	72.4	150,000	95.3	90.7	78.1
175,000	99.5	95.7	83.5	175,000	110.0	104.5	90.4
200,000	113.0	108.0	95.0	200,000	124.0	118.0	102.0

$$\frac{Q}{S}$$

gpm
ft

After Patchick (1967)

Tables 24 and 25 can be used to approximate **T** from **Q/s** or **Q/s** from values of **T** for confined and unconfined aquifers. The tables were derived by substituting certain variables in the Theis formula. Typical pumping periods, well diameters and storage coefficients were assumed. The assumptions have validity, because varying the time of pumping, well diameter and the storage coefficient will not appreciably change the specific capacity. The relationship between **T and Q/s** allows for ease of calculation. **If an estimate needs to be obtained of T or Q/s not directly shown on the table, the procedure is as follows** (Patchick, 1967):

Example, Table 24, confined conditions.

Well diameter = 6 inches; pumping period = 10 days.

Q / s measured in the field = 26.0 gpm / ft.

From Table 24
where

Q / s = 23.3 gpm / ft		**T** =	60,000 gpd / ft
2.2 gpm / ft			5,000 gpd / ft
0.5 gpm / ft			1,000 gpd / ft
then	26.0 gpm / ft	=	66,000 gpd / ft.

In order to calculate transmissivity using equation (64), a series of calculations must occur simultaneously in a list-like-fashion, using a computer program, as follows (r and t are known):

(1)	(2)	(3)	(4)
Estimate theoretical T values.	Solve for u substituting T from column 1 and an estimated S Coefficient into equation (2).	Match W(u) with the calculated u value in column 2 using and interpolating from a list similar to Appendix A.	Calculate Q/s substituting the W(u) value from column 3 and the T value from column 1 into equation (64).
1000	$u = Sr^2 / 4Tt$	W(u)	$Q/s = T4\pi/W(u)$
2000	•	•	•
3000	•	•	•
•	•	•	•
•	•	•	•
•	•	•	•

Once the spreadsheet format has been completed, transmissivity can be interpolated from the calculated Q/s values. The following example demonstrates this method (T using Ogden's method = 101,271 gpd/ft):

Q = 500 gpm, r = 1.0 ft, t = 240 min, s = 9.65 ft, and Q/s = 51.81 gpm / ft. S is assumed to be 0.000198.

Example demonstrating Kasenow's method for estimating T from Q/s.

T gpd/ft	u	W(u)	Q/s gpm/ft
1000	2.2E-06	12.4401	0.70
2000	1.1E-06	13.1332	1.33
3000	7.4E-07	13.5387	1.93
4000	5.6E-07	13.8264	2.52
5000	4.4E-07	14.0495	3.11
6000	3.7E-07	14.2319	3.68
7000	3.2E-07	14.3860	4.25
8000	2.8E-07	14.5195	4.81
9000	2.5E-07	14.6373	5.37
10000	2.2E-07	14.7427	5.92
15000	1.5E-07	15.1482	8.64
20000	1.1E-07	15.4358	11.31
30000	7.4E-08	15.8413	16.53
40000	5.6E-08	16.1290	21.64
50000	4.4E-08	16.3521	26.68
60000	3.7E-08	16.5344	31.66
70000	3.2E-08	16.6886	36.60
80000	2.8E-08	16.8221	41.50
90000	2.5E-08	16.9399	46.36
100000	2.2E-08	17.0453	51.19
125000	1.8E-08	17.2684	63.16
150000	1.5E-08	17.4507	75.01

Q/s = 51.81 gpm/ft; therefore, T can be interpolated between these two values.

The interpolated T = 101,296 gpd / ft, which is comparable to Ogden's solution of T = 101,271 gpd / ft. Fortunately, the "Theis Without Graphs" computer program completes all of the above calculations, including interpolation of T from the Q/s value --- within seconds.

The advantage of using either the Ogden/Theis or Kasenow/Theis Q/s methods to estimate transmissivity, when compared to other specific capacity methods, is accuracy. Simple short-cut equations assume time (t), well radius (r) and storage values (S). The Ogden and Kasenow/Theis methods only request an assumed storage value, which is reasonable, because all other needed variables should be known or collected from field observations. Because (t) and (r) are not assumed, these methods can also be used to calculate transmissivity using observation well data. The drawdown value (s) in the denominator of specific capacity (Q/s) can be an observation well drawdown and the radius, (r), can be an observation well distance. Therefore, transmissivity can be estimated using a single observation well drawdown (Table 27). The Ogden/Theis method has the advantage that it can be completed by hand and in the field when using Appendix A. The Kasenow/Theis method requires a computer.

Table 27. Transmissivity calculated from a single drawdown in three observation wells using the Ogden and Kasenow/Theis methods. $Q = 500$ gpm, $t = 240$ minutes, $r_1 = 200$ ft, $r_2 = 400$ ft, $r_3 = 800$ ft, $s_1 = 3.67$ ft, $s_2 = 2.88$ ft, $s_3 = 2.11$ ft, $S_{assumed} = 0.0002$. Calculated T is approximately = 100,000 to 101,000 gpd/ft using Theis or Cooper-Jacob time-drawdown methods (all observation well drawdowns). Data from Lohman (1972). T units = gpd/ft.

Method	T for r_1	T for r_2	T for r_3
Ogden/Theis	100,622	100,715	99,883
Kasenow/Theis	100,649	100,749	99,924

The Kasenow/Theis method can also be used with equations (32), (33) and (34), which correct for dewatering around the production well. They are defined in Chapter 3.

When the s/b ratio < 25% use equation (32):

1- [(s/b) (.19)] = relative Q/s as a percent.   (32)

When s/b ratio ≥ 25% and ≤ 75% use equation (33):

1- [((s/b) -.20)) (.54)] = relative Q/s as a percent.   (33)

When the s/b ratio > 75% use equation (34):

1- [((s/b) -.64)) (1.24)] = relative Q/s as a percent.   (34)

For consistent units:
s = the drawdown in the pumping well, and
b = the aquifer thickness.

Both methods can be used with the Kozeny equation to correct for partial penetration, if pumping has continued for a reasonable length of time (Turcan, 1962). The Kozeny equation is defined on the following page.

CORRECTING Q/s FOR PARTIAL PENETRATION OF A PUMPING WELL

Correcting drawdown for transient partial penetration effects is often an impossible task.

The Kozeny equation offers reasonable results, especially after extensive pumping periods that approach steady-state conditions (Turcan, 1962):

$$Q/s_{corrected} = \frac{Q/s_{field}}{\left[\dfrac{L_s}{b}\right]\left[1 + 7\sqrt{\left[\dfrac{r_w}{2b\left[\dfrac{L_s}{b}\right]}\right]\left[\cos\left((\pi)\dfrac{\dfrac{L_s}{b}}{2}\right)\right]}\right]}$$

Where

$Q/s_{corrected}$ = the corrected specific capacity = gpm / ft

Q/s_{field} = the field measured specific capacity
= the specific capacity at partial penetration = gpm / ft

L_s = the length of the well screen = ft

b = the aquifer thickness = ft

r_w = the well radius = ft

The above equation assumes no well loss and a homogeneous system, and may be inaccurate when the aquifer thickness is small, the L_s / b ratio is large, and when the well radius is large (Turcan, 1962 and Driscoll, 1986).

EIGHT
THEIS WITHOUT GRAPHS

A Computer Program By

Michael Kasenow and Paul Pare

LICENSE AGREEMENT

Copyright Notice

This software is protected by copyright law; therefore, you must treat this software **just like a book**. By saying **"just like a book"**, the authors mean, that there can be no possibility of this software being used at one location while it is being used at another location. Just like the same copy of a book can't be read by two different people in two different locations at the same time.

You have the non-exclusive right to use the enclosed program(s). You may not distribute copies of the program(s) or documentation of the program(s) to others. You may not assign, sublicense, or transfer this license without the written permission of the developers. You may not rent, lease, modify or translate the program(s) without prior written permission of the developers. You may not incorporate all or part of the program(s) into another product without the permission of the developers.

Backup

You may make two (2) copies of the program(s) solely for backup purposes.

Warranty

Once the program(s) are in the possession of the purchaser --- **absolutely no refunds**. In the event of notification of lost, defective or stolen diskettes, the lost, defective or stolen diskettes will be replaced. The warranty requires proof of purchase and is limited to replacement and shall not encompass any direct or indirect damages, including but not limited to loss of profit, interruption of business, and special incidental, consequential or other similar claims.

<u>Disclaimer</u>

Neither the developer(s) of this software nor any person or organization acting on behalf of him (them) makes any warranty, express or implied, with respect to this software; or assumes any liabilities with respect to the use, misuse, or inability to use this software, or interpretation, or misinterpretation, of any results obtained from this software, or for damages resulting from the use of this software.

REQUIREMENTS

A PC compatible computer with 640 K memory, a printer that compliments your computer --- and common sense. A geologic or hydrogeologic background is obviously an asset.

Theis Without Graphs is written in Turbo Pascal.

WELCOME

Theis Without Graphs (TWG) is easy to use. Just press the correct number on your computer key board relative to the information that the program is requesting. You will eventually be asked to enter data, again, simply respond correctly. If the TWG editor is needed to input data, again, follow the instructions correctly and you should have no problem in doing so. Like any software package a learning curve will be required by the user. Give yourself the time to gain the experience and TWG should become a welcome addition to your hydrogeologic software collection.

The TWG advantage:

- Quick and easy to use.
- Many solution methods to substantiate your results.
- Theis time-drawdown can be solved without the Theis curve, but this is "no blackbox". The Theis assumptions can be verified without curve matching!
- Theis distance-drawdown can be easily used as a solution method!
- Both transmissivity and storativity can be estimated using residual drawdown data from observation wells.
- Specific capacity solutions can be adjusted for well efficiency, dewatering and partial penetration.
- The limit of the cone of depression is calculated.

EXAMPLE: TWG OUTPUT

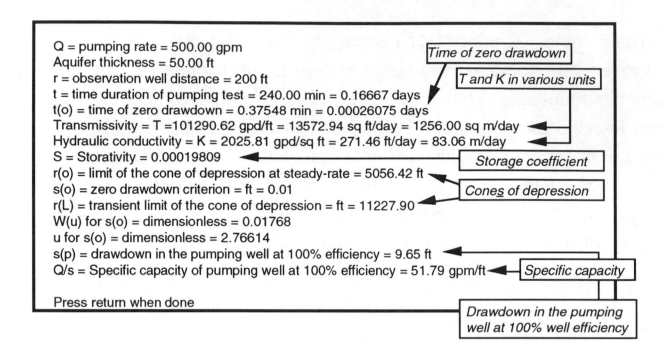

Q = pumping rate = 500.00 gpm
Aquifer thickness = 50.00 ft
r = observation well distance = 200 ft
t = time duration of pumping test = 240.00 min = 0.16667 days
t(o) = time of zero drawdown = 0.37548 min = 0.00026075 days
Transmissivity = T =101290.62 gpd/ft = 13572.94 sq ft/day = 1256.00 sq m/day
Hydraulic conductivity = K = 2025.81 gpd/sq ft = 271.46 ft/day = 83.06 m/day
S = Storativity = 0.00019809
r(o) = limit of the cone of depression at steady-rate = 5056.42 ft
s(o) = zero drawdown criterion = ft = 0.01
r(L) = transient limit of the cone of depression = ft = 11227.90
W(u) for s(o) = dimensionless = 0.01768
u for s(o) = dimensionless = 2.76614
s(p) = drawdown in the pumping well at 100% efficiency = 9.65 ft
Q/s = Specific capacity of pumping well at 100% efficiency = 51.79 gpm/ft

Press return when done

Time of zero drawdown

T and K in various units

Storage coefficient

Cones of depression

Specific capacity

Drawdown in the pumping well at 100% well efficiency

USING THIS CHAPTER

Chapter 8 offers instructions relative to the use of TWG. We hope that this section, like the TWG program, is easy to follow. We will communicate with you as if we are using the program together. Your computer screen will be represented by a rectangle box and the program options will be displayed within the box. *Italics* are used in the box representing your computer screen when we wish to communicate with you. ***Italics*** indicate instructions that will not appear on your screen.

< RETURN > : means enter return after entering the requested data.

When ***IMPORTANT!*** appears in the instructions, please pay special attention to what we are trying to communicate to you.

An example of the manual instructions appears below:

138

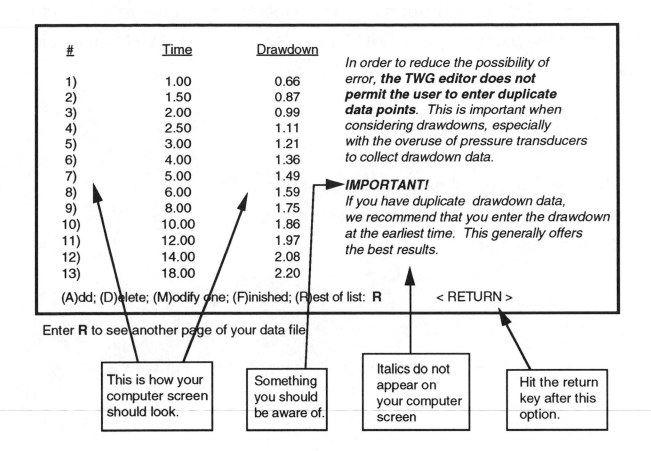

#	Time	Drawdown
1)	1.00	0.66
2)	1.50	0.87
3)	2.00	0.99
4)	2.50	1.11
5)	3.00	1.21
6)	4.00	1.36
7)	5.00	1.49
8)	6.00	1.59
9)	8.00	1.75
10)	10.00	1.86
11)	12.00	1.97
12)	14.00	2.08
13)	18.00	2.20

*In order to reduce the possibility of error, **the TWG editor does not permit the user to enter duplicate data points**. This is important when considering drawdowns, especially with the overuse of pressure transducers to collect drawdown data.*

IMPORTANT!
If you have duplicate drawdown data, we recommend that you enter the drawdown at the earliest time. This generally offers the best results.

(A)dd; (D)elete; (M)odify one; (F)inished; (R)est of list: **R**   < RETURN >

Enter **R** to see another page of your data file

This is how your computer screen should look.

Something you should be aware of.

Italics do not appear on your computer screen

Hit the return key after this option.

When **saving a file** in TWG use up to eight characters and do not add on the .dd extension, that is done automatically by TWG. Files with .dd extensions in your directory indicate TWG data files.

When **retrieving a file** in TWG do not add on the extension.

Example:

Saving a file: > Lohman   (6 characters)

File in directory: Lohman.dd   (6 characters + extension)

Retrieving a file   > Lohman   (6 characters)

To **start Theis Without Graphs**, place the disk into your favorite drive and at the prompt type in TWG for English units and TWGM for metric units:

> **TWG**

The opening page should appear on your screen.
Press any key to retrieve the main menu.
Enjoy the program.

EXAMPLE DATA

The data to be used to demonstrate most of the TWG program is from Lohman (1972). More data will be introduced later when needed.

For Time-Drawdown and Distance-Drawdown

Q = 500 gpm

drawdown = ft, r = 200 ft, 400 ft, and 800 ft

TIME (min)	DRAWDOWN (r=200 ft)	DRAWDOWN (r=400 ft)	DRAWDOWN (r=800 ft)
1.0	0.66	0.16	0.0046
1.5	0.87	0.27	0.02
2.0	0.99	0.38	0.04
2.5	1.11	0.46	0.07
3.0	1.21	0.53	0.09
4.0	1.36	0.67	0.16
5.0	1.49	0.77	0.22
6.0	1.59	0.87	0.27
8.0	1.75	0.99	0.37
10.0	1.86	1.12	0.46
12.0	1.97	1.21	0.53
14.0	2.08	1.26	0.59
18.0	2.20	1.43	0.72
24.0	2.36	1.58	0.87
30.0	2.49	1.70	0.95
40.0	2.65	1.88	1.12
50.0	2.78	2.00	1.23
60.0	2.88	2.11	1.32
80.0	3.04	2.24	1.49
100.0	3.16	2.38	1.62
120.0	3.28	2.49	1.70
150.0	3.42	2.62	1.83
180.0	3.51	2.72	1.94
210.0	3.61	2.81	2.03
240.0	3.67	2.88	2.11

Lohman's results using the Theis Distance-Drawdown Method (three observation wells):

T = 102,476 gpd / ft and S = 0.00020

Results using the Theis Time-Drawdown Method (single observation well):

T = 100,471 gpd / ft and S = 0.00020

Insert the TWG disk into your favorite drive and at the prompt type in TWG:
The opening page to the program should look like the one below.

> TWG

WELCOME TO THEIS WITHOUT GRAPHS

Version 1.0

An Analytical Groundwater Program By

Michael Kasenow and Paul Pare

Copyright 1993, 1994

Water Resources Publications

Press any key to continue

After striking any key, the TWG main menu should appear.

THEIS WITHOUT GRAPHS

Please Select A Method For Estimating Aquifer Parameters

1) Theis Time-Drawdown

2) Theis Distance-Drawdown

3) Theis Recovery

4) Ogden / Theis Solution

5) Kasenow / Theis Solution

6) Step-Drawdown Analysis

7) Model a pump test

8) Exit   Please enter menu option: 1   < RETURN >

At Any Menu Option You Can Type "Q"; This Will Take You Back To This Menu

---

We will begin analyzing the aquifer with our data using **Theis Time-Drawdown.**

Enter 1 and < RETURN >.

If you get "stuck" in any module, type in "Q" where a "Y/N" option is requested, and you will be taken back to this menu by the program.

142

THEIS TIME-DRAWDOWN

The next page should read:

The aquifer is suspected of being

1) Confined

2) Unconfined

Choice: 1   < RETURN >

Assume that we have carefully examined the well log and suspect that our aquifer is confined. Select: 1 and < RETURN >.

The next page should read:

---

1) Interpolate drawdowns in Z(u) method

2) Do not interpolate drawdowns

Choice: 2   < RETURN >

Generally select 2, unless you wish to examine **T** and **S** for all of the data. You can always return to the program to do this.

The data entry page should appear on your screen. Simply respond correctly:

Enter pumping well discharge = Q = gpm: 500

Enter observation well distance = ft: 200

Enter total time duration of pumping test = t = min: 240

Enter pumping well radius = r(p) = ft (1.0 is default): 1

Is this correct (Y/N): Y   < RETURN >

This information is used to determine the drawdown in the pumping well at 100% well efficiency. If you wish to use 1 by default, you must enter 1 at this option.

The file menu should next appear on your screen:

(O)pen an existing file or (M)ake new file: M

Name of save file (up to 8 letters): Lohman

IMPORTANT!

If you type in the wrong letter by mistake, you might get "stuck" here, and will have to type in "Q" to start over.

Just pay attention to what you're doing! You only have two choices: M or O.

Do not add an extension. If the filename you have selected is already in use you will be given the following message:

That filename already used! Rewrite (Y/N):

Answer carefully and correctly.

If you have already created the file then enter (O) at

(O)pen an existing file or (M)ake new file: O

You will then be asked to enter your file name and the program will retrieve it and allow you to edit the file in the TWG EDITOR.

The **TWG EDITOR** should next appear on your screen and look like this:

Time   Drawdown

    Enter time: 1.00

    Enter drawdown: .66   < RETURN >

> *Always enter **time as minutes**
> and **drawdown as feet** (for English version).
> Enter the first set of data points and then
> **return**. The editor will immediately transform
> itself as it appears in the next frame.*

Remember: time = minutes and drawdown = feet.

Time   Drawdown
1)   1.00   0.66

> *To **add** more data enter **A before each entry** and **return**.
> To **delete** data enter **D** and **return**.
> To **modify** one data set enter **M** and **return**.
> If you wish to see another page of the file enter **R** and **return**.
> When you are **finished** enter **F** and **return**.*

(A)dd; (D)elete; (M)odify one; (F)inished; (R)est of list: **A**   < RETURN >

    Enter time: 1.5   < RETURN >
    Enter drawdown: .87   < RETURN >

Continue to enter the data file until finished...

#	Time	Drawdown
1)	1.00	0.66
2)	1.50	0.87
3)	2.00	0.99
4)	2.50	1.11
5)	3.00	1.21
6)	4.00	1.36
7)	5.00	1.49
8)	6.00	1.59
9)	8.00	1.75
10)	10.00	1.86
11)	12.00	1.97
12)	14.00	2.08
13)	18.00	2.20

*In order to reduce the possibility of error, **the TWG editor does not permit the user to enter duplicate data points**. This is important when considering drawdowns, especially with the overuse of pressure transducers to collect drawdown data.*

IMPORTANT!
If you have duplicate drawdown data, we recommend that you enter the drawdown at the earliest time. This generally offers the best results.

(A)dd; (D)elete; (M)odify one; (F)inished; (R)est of list: **R**   < RETURN >

Enter **R** to see another page of your data file.

The second page of your data file should look like this:

#	Time	Drawdown
14)	24.00	2.36
15)	30.00	2.49
16)	40.00	2.65
17)	50.00	2.78
18)	60.00	2.88
19)	80.00	3.04
20)	100.00	3.16
21)	120.00	3.28
22)	150.00	3.42
23)	180.00	3.51
24)	210.00	3.61
25)	240.00	3.67

(A)dd; (D)elete; (M)odify one; (F)inished; (R)est of list: **F**   < RETURN >

After the data file is complete enter **F** for the calculations to begin...a few seconds will pass...

...and the **results** for the Z(u) method should be displayed on your screen:

t min	s ft	Z(u)	u	W(u)	T gpd/ft	S
2	0.99	0.6667	1.0E-01	1.794	103842	0.000199
3	1.21	0.7190	6.3E-02	2.249	106503	0.000187
4	1.36	0.7279	5.7E-02	2.344	98742	0.000209
5	1.49	0.7450	4.6E-02	2.543	97784	0.000210
6	1.59	0.7610	3.7E-02	2.748	99042	0.000206
8	1.75	0.7771	2.9E-02	2.981	97615	0.000212
10	1.86	0.8011	1.9E-02	3.388	104375	0.000187
12	1.97	0.8071	1.7E-02	3.506	101962	0.000195
24	2.36	0.8347	9.0E-03	4.140	100530	0.000202
60	2.88	0.8646	3.5E-03	5.093	101330	0.000195
80	3.04	0.8717	2.6E-03	5.382	101452	0.000195
100	3.16	0.8797	1.8E-03	5.748	104232	0.000173
120	3.28	0.8780	1.9E-03	5.668	99010	0.000214

Press any key to continue

< RETURN > in order to see the rest of the calculated results and the final **T** and **S** values for the aquifer:

The last page of the calculations and final **T** and **S** values should be displayed:

t min	s ft	Z(u)	u	W(u)	T gpd/ft	S
240	3.67	0.8937	8.4E-04	6.511	101652	0.000189
				Average ==>	101291	0.000198

The TWG editor allows the user to return to the list with the calculations, and it also allows the user to calculate particular intervals within the list (more on that later). The TWG editor also allows the user to return to the editor in order to retrieve the file, do some editing, and recalculate the data. All of this can be completed with very little effort.

Do you wish to see list again (Y/N): N   < RETURN >
Do you wish to look at particular intervals (Y/N): N   < RETURN >

Do you wish to return to the editor (Y/N): N   < RETURN >

It should be obvious when observing the many calculated values of **T** and **S** that the **Theis assumptions appear to be valid; therefore, we should continue with the program.**

You should then be asked if you want a printout...

Do you want to print the results (Y/N): Y   < RETURN >

IMPORTANT!

*A printout of the above calculations is obtained using the **print screen** command, because they really are not necessary. The question:*

Do you want to print the results (Y/N):

refers to the final output containing the parameter results.

...then for the aquifer thickness...if you know it...

Do you know the aquifer thickness in feet (Y/N): Y   < RETURN >

The aquifer thickness = b = ft: 50   < RETURN >

Is this correct (Y/N): Y   < RETURN >

This question is asked in order to calculate hydraulic conductivity from transmissivity using the following formula:

$K = T/b$ *where K = hydraulic conductivity.*

If you don't know the aquifer thickness, the program ignores this calculation.

...then for a drawdown criterion to calculate the limit of the transient cone of depression.

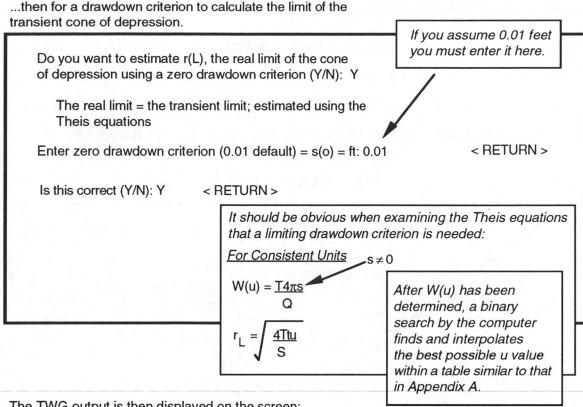

Do you want to estimate r(L), the real limit of the cone of depression using a zero drawdown criterion (Y/N): Y

    The real limit = the transient limit; estimated using the Theis equations

Enter zero drawdown criterion (0.01 default) = s(o) = ft: 0.01   < RETURN >

Is this correct (Y/N): Y   < RETURN >

> If you assume 0.01 feet you must enter it here.

It should be obvious when examining the Theis equations that a limiting drawdown criterion is needed:

For Consistent Units $s \neq 0$

$$W(u) = \frac{T4\pi s}{Q}$$

$$r_L = \sqrt{\frac{4Ttu}{S}}$$

After W(u) has been determined, a binary search by the computer finds and interpolates the best possible u value within a table similar to that in Appendix A.

The TWG output is then displayed on the screen:

Q = pumping rate = 500.00 gpm   *Theis - Z(u) Time-Drawdown output*
Aquifer thickness = 50.00 ft
r = observation well distance = 200 ft
t = time duration of pumping test = 240.00 min = 0.16667 days
t(o) = time of zero drawdown = 0.37548 min = 0.00026075 days
Slope = 1.30 ft
Transmissivity = T =101290.62 gpd/ft = 13572.94 sq ft/day = 1256.00 sq m/day
Hydraulic conductivity = K = 2025.81 gpd/sq ft = 271.46 ft/day = 83.06 m/day
S = Storativity = 0.00019809
r(o) = limit of the cone of depression at steady-rate = 5056.42 ft
s(o) = zero drawdown criterion = ft = 0.01
r(L) = transient limit of the cone of depression = ft = 11227.90
W(u) for s(o) = dimensionless = 0.01768
u for s(o) = dimensionless = 2.76614
s(p) = drawdown in the pumping well at 100% efficiency = 9.65 ft
Q/s = Specific capacity of pumping well at 100% efficiency = 51.79 gpm/ft
Press return when done

After pressing return, a printout with the same information is released and you will be transferred **back to the TWG Main Menu.**

A DEMONSTRATION OF THE ACCURACY OF THE Z(u) METHOD

The program interpolates the best answers for u and W(u) relative to the Z(u) index; therefore, the Z(u) method, when used in this way, is probably more accurate than other methods that apply the Theis solution. This can be demonstrated by using recharge data from Figure 14.

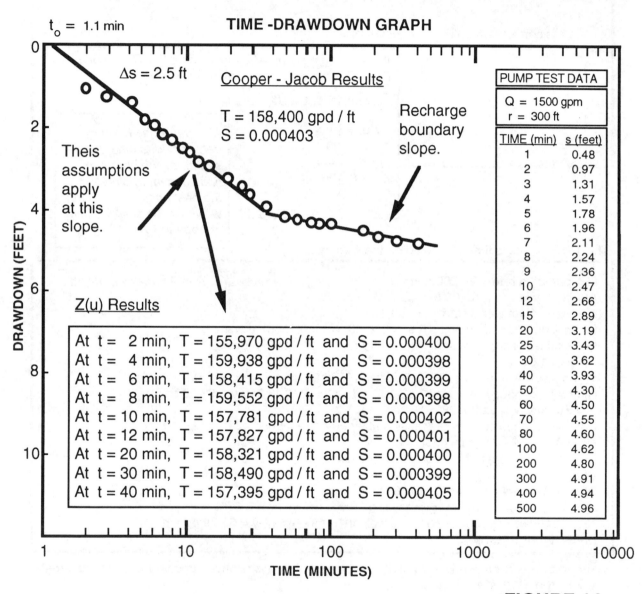

FIGURE 14

After the pump test constants were entered and the time - drawdown file created, the Z(u) solution calculated the following parameters:

t min	s ft	Z(u)	u	W(u)	T gpd/ft	S
2	0.97	0.4948	3.1E-01	0.880	155970	0.000400
4	1.57	0.6178	1.5E-01	1.461	159938	0.000398
6	1.96	0.6684	1.0E-01	1.806	158415	0.000399
8	2.24	0.7009	7.6E-02	2.079	159552	0.000398
10	2.47	0.7206	6.2E-02	2.267	157781	0.000402
12	2.66	0.7368	5.1E-02	2.442	157827	0.000401
20	3.19	0.7743	3.1E-02	2.938	158321	0.000400
30	3.62	0.7983	2.0E-02	3.338	158490	0.000399
40	3.93	0.8117	1.6E-02	3.598	157395	0.000405
50	4.30	0.7977	2.1E-02	3.325	132925	0.000565

Press any key to continue

Fortunately the Z(u) solution allows the user to calculate a **specific interval of parameters**.

It should be obvious by observing late parameter values that recharge is occurring (beginning at t = 50 min).

t min	s ft	Z(u)	u	W(u)	T gpd/ft	S
60	4.50	0.8044	1.8E-02	3.453	131911	0.000591
80	4.60	0.8543	5.0E-03	5.725	176559	0.000292
100	4.62	0.9307	2.5E-05	10.007	372322	0.000004
200	4.80	0.9625	5.4E-09	18.462	661179	0.000000
400	4.94	0.9700	5.4E-11	23.072	802847	0.000000
				Average ==>	246762	0.000337

Do you wish to see the list again (Y/N): N
Do you wish to look at particular intervals (Y/N): Y

Press any key to continue

Select this option and another screen will appear which will allow you to calculate the desired interval.

Enter "Y" and < RETURN >

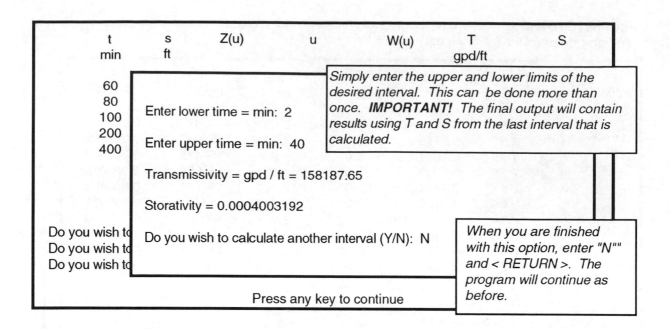

t	s	Z(u)	u	W(u)	T	S
min	ft				gpd/ft	

60
80
100
200
400

Enter lower time = min: 2

Enter upper time = min: 40

Transmissivity = gpd / ft = 158187.65

Storativity = 0.0004003192

Do you wish to calculate another interval (Y/N): N

Do you wish to
Do you wish to
Do you wish to

*Simply enter the upper and lower limits of the desired interval. This can be done more than once. **IMPORTANT!** The final output will contain results using T and S from the last interval that is calculated.*

When you are finished with this option, enter "N"" and < RETURN >. The program will continue as before.

Press any key to continue

T and S using the interval option are equal to 158,187 gpd / ft and 0.000400, respectively, which confirms the results offered by Figure 14. The interval option is a very powerful tool and probably unique to the TWG program.

THEIS-Z(u) DISTANCE-DRAWDOWN METHOD

To use the Theis-Z(u) distance-drawdown solution **enter 2** at the TWG main menu...

The next page should ask you for the aquifer type.

The aquifer is suspected of being

1) Confined

2) Unconfined

3) Using a recovery method

Choice: 1   < RETURN >

The pump test data input page should next appear.

Enter discharge = Q = gpm: 500   < RETURN >

Enter time of pump test or desired drawdown = t = min: 240   < RETURN >

Is this correct (Y/N): Y   < RETURN >

(M)ake a file and call it "Disdraw".
At the TWG editor you will be asked to enter the **observation well distances**, the **drawdowns at the pump test time** you entered, and at **1/2 the pump test time**.

#	Distance	Drawdown	Drawdown at half time

Enter distance in ft: 200

Enter drawdown at 240.00 min in ft: 3.67

Enter drawdown at 120.00 min in ft: 2.88

The example data is from Lohman (1972).

Please enter < RETURN > after each entry.

(A)dd; (D)elete; (M)odify one; (F)inished; (R)est of List:

Repeat the data entry for all of the wells.

#	Distance	Drawdown	Drawdown at half time
1	200	3.67	3.28
2	400	2.88	2.49
3	800	2.11	1.70

The number of wells that you can enter should not exceed 15.

(A)dd; (D)elete; (M)odify one; (F)inished; (R)est of List: F   < RETURN >

Next, the **T** and **S** values should be displayed:

r ft	s ft	Z(u)	u	W(u)	T gpd/ft	S
200.00	3.67	0.8937	8.4E-04	6.511	101652	0.000189
400.00	2.88	0.8646	3.5E-03	5.093	101329	0.000195
800.00	2.11	0.8057	1.8E-02	3.477	94414	0.000232
				Average ==>	99132	0.000205

Press any key to continue

The next few pages will be identical to the Theis-Z(u) Time- Drawdown pages that ask you for **aquifer thickness, r(L) data, if you want a printout, etc...**

...then the final output will be displayed and printed if requested to do so.

Output for Theis-Z(u) Distance-Drawdown Method

Q = pumping rate = 500.00 gpm
t = time duration of pump test = min = 240.00 = 0.16666 days
Aquifer thickness = 50.00 ft
Slope = 2.66 ft
Transmissivity = T = 99132.05 gpd/ft = 13283.69 sq ft/day = 1229.24 sq m/day
Hydraulic conductivity = K = 1982.64 gpd/sq ft = 265.67 ft/day = 81.29 m/day
S = Storativity = 0.00020543
r(o) = limit of the cone of depression at steady-rate = 4912.06 ft
s(o) = zero drawdown criterion = ft = 0.01
r(L) = transient limit of the cone of depression = ft = 10944.43
W(u) for s(o) = Dimensionless = 0.01730
u for s(o) = Dimensionless = 2.78497
s(p) = drawdown in pumping well at 100% efficiency = 9.83 ft
Q/s = Specific capacity of pumping well at 100% efficiency = 50.86 gpm/ft

Press Return when done

< RETURN > should bring you back to the TWG main menu.

155

THE THEIS RECOVERY METHOD

The Theis Recovery module works in a similar manner as the Theis -Z(u) Time-Drawdown module, except, that the Theis Recovery solution uses residual drawdown data. When entering data at the editor remember that t in minutes = t' minutes, and s in feet = s' feet. In other words, simply enter the data as t' and s'. TWG does all other needed calculations.

Pump test results: **T = 10,950 gpd/ft; S = 0.000017**
Observation well 1, **r = 824 ft, Q = 220 gpm**
Source: Bruin and Hudson (1955), Kasenow (1993)
Aquifer thickness: 18 ft
(Partial data base)

Time since pump test started t = minutes	Time since pumping stopped t' = minutes	Ratio t / t'	Residual drawdown s' = feet
500	0	0	10.9
522	22	23.73	7.37
524	24	21.83	7.15
526	26	20.23	6.99
528	28	18.86	6.97
530	30	17.67	6.79
534	34	15.71	6.52
538	38	14.16	6.35
546	46	11.87	5.85
550	50	11.00	5.70
560	60	9.33	5.35
565	65	8.69	5.17
570	70	8.14	5.13
590	90	6.56	4.58
600	100	6.00	4.41
620	120	5.17	3.98
630	130	4.85	3.86
640	140	4.57	3.69
650	150	4.33	3.62
660	160	4.13	3.33
670	170	3.94	3.29
680	180	3.78	3.26
770	270	2.85	2.54
800	300	2.67	2.33
830	330	2.52	2.13
850	350	2.43	2.17

Kasenow (1993) has developed a method to solve for the storage coefficient using residual drawdown observation well data. As you test TWG you will find this method to be reasonably accurate, because it is independent of the time-drawdown pump test graph.

The data on the previous page is from Kasenow (1993). Bruin and Hudson originally calculated values of T and S at 10,950 gpd/ft and 0.000017, respectively, using recovery data. They obtained the same results using pump test data. Walton (1962) calculated T and S equal to 10,100 gpd/ft and 0.00002, respectively, using pump test data.

Get into **Theis Recovery** at the TWG main menu by entering 3 and returning. The next frame will offer two choices:

1) Solve for a pumping well
2) Solve for an observation well

Choice 1 solves for Transmissivity (the storage coefficient cannot be calculated because the effective well radius is usually unknown).

Choice 2 solves for both Transmissivity and the storage coefficient using residual drawdown data.

Select choice 2 and begin to enter in your constants, which are determined from the pump test:

Enter pumping well discharge = Q = gpm: 220

Enter pumping well radius = r(p) = ft (1.0 is default): 1.0

Enter total time duration of pump test = t = min: 500

Enter observation well distance = ft: 824

Enter drawdown when the pump was turned off = ft: 10.9

Is this correct (Y/N): Y

Please < RETURN >
after entering each
pump test constant.

*When solving **T** for a **pumping well**, this value is not extremely important, and a "dummy" variable can be used.*

*This is needed to solve for t(o)', which is used to solve the storage coefficient. It is equal to zero recovery. **IMPORTANT!** this value must be a transient value, not steady-state. If the pump test has continued into steady-state, then select the last transient value and its corresponding time, and assume that the transient pump test ended at that interval.*

< RETURN > after entering "Y".

You will then be transferred to the editor.

(M)ake a file and call it "Gridrec".

When entering data into the editor **time = minutes = t'** and **drawdown = feet = s'**.

Remember, this is a Theis solution method; therefore, you should enter all of the residual drawdown data into the editor. You do not need to worry about constructing $\Delta s'$, but you will have the opportunity to select intervals as you did in the Theis Time-Drawdown Module.

158

At the editor (M)ake a file for recovery: example, call this one "GRIDREC".

#	Time	Drawdown	
			IMPORTANT!!
1)	22	7.37	
2)	24	7.15	***Time = t' = minutes***
3)	26	6.99	***Drawdown = s' = ft***
4)	28	6.97	
5)	30	6.79	
6)	34	6.52	
7)	38	6.35	
8)	46	5.85	
9)	50	5.70	
10)	60	5.35	
11)	65	5.17	
12)	70	5.13	
13)	90	4.58	

(A)dd; (D)elete; (M)odify one; (F)inished; (R)est of list: R   < RETURN >

#	Time	Drawdown	
			Time = t' = minutes
			Drawdown = s' = ft
14)	100	4.41	
15)	120	3.98	
16)	130	3.86	
17)	140	3.69	
18)	150	3.62	
19)	160	3.33	
20)	170	3.29	
21)	180	3.26	
22)	270	2.54	
23)	300	2.33	
24)	330	2.13	
25)			

(A)dd; (D)elete; (M)odify one; (F)inished; (R)est of list: F   < RETURN >

t min	t' min	Ratio t/t'	s'	Slope ft	T gpd/ft	S
522.00	22.00	23.73	7.37	5.36	10837.77	0.0000154
524.00	24.00	21.83	7.15	5.34	10877.78	0.0000152
526.00	26.00	20.23	6.99	5.35	10851.67	0.0000153
528.00	28.00	18.86	6.97	5.46	10628.36	0.0000165
530.00	30.00	17.67	6.79	5.44	10667.86	0.0000163
534.00	34.00	15.71	6.52	5.45	10654.49	0.0000164
538.00	38.00	14.16	6.35	5.52	10527.56	0.0000171
546.00	46.00	11.87	5.85	5.44	10667.21	0.0000163
550.00	50.00	11.00	5.70	5.47	10611.24	0.0000166
560.00	60.00	9.33	5.35	5.52	10530.79	0.0000171
565.00	65.00	8.69	5.17	5.51	10550.28	0.0000169
570.00	70.00	8.14	5.13	5.63	10311.48	0.0000184

This column allows for a visual inspection of Δs' relative to the data points

t min	t' min	Ratio t/t'	s'	Slope ft	T gpd/ft	S
590.00	90.00	6.56	4.58	5.61	10355.61	0.0000181
600.00	100.00	6.00	4.41	5.67	10248.30	0.0000188
620.00	120.00	5.17	3.98	5.58	10407.85	0.0000178
630.00	130.00	4.85	3.86	5.63	10312.92	0.0000184
640.00	140.00	4.57	3.69	5.59	10389.11	0.0000179
650.00	150.00	4.33	3.62	5.68	10217.30	0.0000190
660.00	160.00	4.13	3.33	5.41	10733.88	0.0000159
670.00	170.00	3.94	3.29	5.52	10514.88	0.0000172
680.00	180.00	3.78	3.26	5.65	10284.02	0.0000185
770.00	270.00	2.85	2.54	5.58	10407.00	0.0000178
800.00	300.00	2.67	2.33	5.47	10618.14	0.0000166
830.00	330.00	2.52	2.13	5.32	10922.43	0.0000149
				Average ===>	10547.00	0.0000170

Do you wish to see list again (Y/N): N < RETURN >
Do you wish to look at particular intervals (Y/N): Y < RETURN >

t	t'	Ratio		Slope	T	
min	min	t/t'	s'	ft	gpd/ft	S
522.00	22.00					
524.00	24.00					
526.00	26.00					
528.00	28.00					
530.00	30.00					
534.00	34.00					
538.00	38.00					
546.00	46.00					
550.00	50.00					
560.00	60.00					
565.00	65.00					
570.00	70.00					

Enter lower t' = min : 28   < RETURN >   ◄—— **IMPORTANT!**
Use t' for interval
Enter upper t' = min: 300   < RETURN >   ◄——   **minutes.**

Transmissivity = T = gpd/ft =   10481.91

Storativity = 0.0000173661

Do you wish to do another interval (Y/N): N   < RETURN >

IMPORTANT!

The T and S values calculated using this option will be the T and S values reported in the final output, and used in all other calculations that require T and S.

t	t'	Ratio		Slope	T	
min	min	t/t'	s'	ft	gpd/ft	S
590.00	90.00					
600.00	100.00					
620.00	120.00					
630.00	130.00					
640.00	140.00					
650.00	150.00					
660.00	160.00					
670.00	170.00					
680.00	180.00					
770.00	270.00					
800.00	300.00					
830.00	330.00					

Enter lower t' = min : 28   < RETURN >

Enter upper t' = min: 300   < RETURN >

Transmissivity = T = gpd/ft = 10481.91

Storativity = 0.0000173661

Do you wish to do another interval (Y/N): N   < RETURN >

Average ===>   10547.00   0.0000170

Do you wish to see list again (Y/N): N   < RETURN >
Do you wish to look at particular intervals (Y/N): Y   < RETURN >
Do you wish to look at list again (Y/N): N   < RETURN >   ◄——   *You will then*
Do you wish to return to editor (Y/N): N   < RETURN >   ◄——   *be given these*
options.

161

You will next be asked for more information: "aquifer thickness?", "zero drawdown criterion?", etc... The final output will then be presented.

Q = pumping rate = 220.00 gpm   *Residual Drawdown Output*
Observation well distance = r = 824.00 ft
t = duration of pump test = min = 500.00 = days = 0.3472
t(o)' = time of zero recovery = 5.40 min = 0.0037 days
Aquifer thickness = 18.00 ft
Slope = 5.54 ft
(t / t') at origin = 1.04
Transmissivity = T = 10481.91 gpd/ft = 1404.58 sq ft/day = 129.98 sq m/day
Hydraulic conductivity = K = 582.33 gpd/sq ft = 78.03 ft/day = 23.88 m/day
S = Storativity = 0.00001737
r(o) = limit of cone of depression at steady-rate = 7929.27 ft
s(o) = zero drawdown criterion = ft = 0.01
r(L) = transient limit of cone of depression = ft = 21089.44
W(u) for s(o) = Dimensionless = 0.00416
u for s(o) = Dimensionless = 3.96850
s(p) = drawdown in pumping well at 100% efficiency = 43.21 ft
Q/s = Specific capacity of pumping well at 100% efficiency = 5.09 gpm/ft

Press return when done

You will again be brought back to the TWG main menu.

THEIS WITHOUT GRAPHS

Please Select A Method For Estimating Aquifer Parameters

1) Theis Time-Drawdown

2) Theis Distance-Drawdown

3) Theis Recovery

4) Ogden / Theis Solution

5) Kasenow / Theis Solution

6) Step-Drawdown Analysis

7) Model a pump test

8) Exit

At Any Menu Option You Can Type "Q"; This Will Take You Back To This Menu

Please enter menu option: < RETURN >

ENTERING UNCONFINED AQUIFER DATA

Shortly after selecting your solution method you will be given the following choices. If the aquifer data is from an unconfined system and the drawdowns need to be corrected --- select 2. If the drawdowns do not need to be corrected select 1.

The aquifer is suspected of being

1) Confined

2) Unconfined ◄―――――――――――― *Make this selection if the drawdowns need to be corrected for dewatering.*

3) Using a recovery method

Choice: 2

Even if you make the wrong selection, the following options are offered:

Do you want your drawdowns corrected when entered?

1) No, drawdowns have already been corrected

2) Yes, please have drawdowns corrected when entered

Choice: 2   < RETURN >

Is this correct (Y/N): Y   < RETURN >

** Aquifer thickness must be entered in order to correct drawdowns **

Do you know aquifer thickness in feet (Y/N): Y   < RETURN >

The aquifer thickness = b = ft: 26   < RETURN >

Is this correct (Y/N): Y   < RETURN >

Select 2 only if the drawdowns need to be corrected.

If you do not know the aquifer thickness, the program will not correct the drawdowns, but it will still accept the data.

IMPORTANT!

Drawdown data is saved as entered.
If you are correcting drawdowns now, you will need to correct them for each subsequent solution method you use --- after you retrieve your file.

After you have completed these options, the program will continue as before.

OGDEN / THEIS SOLUTION

For our example the aquifer is confined. We will be using the Lohman data as calculated by Theis-Z(u): $s(p)$ = the drawdown in the production well = 9.65 ft; t = time of pump test = 240 min; Q = the production well discharge = 500 gpm; and $r(p)$ = the radius of the pumping well = 1.0 ft (by default). Transmissivity was estimated to be about 101,290.62 gpd/ft and storativity was estimated to be about 0.00019809. The storage coefficient cannot be estimated with any certainty using specific capacity data, due to lack of knowledge of the effective radius of the pumping well, but transmissivity can be approximated for a well that fully penetrates the aquifer at 100% well efficiency. Let's use the following options to prove this little hypothesis.

To use the Ogden/Theis method enter **4 at the TWG main menu**.

THEIS WITHOUT GRAPHS
Please Select A Method For Estimating Aquifer Parameters

1) Theis Time-Drawdown

2) Theis Distance-Drawdown

3) Theis Recovery

4) Ogden / Theis Solution

5) Kasenow / Theis Solution

6) Step-Drawdown Analysis

7) Model a pump test

8) Exit   Please enter menu option: 4   < RETURN >

> At Any Menu Option You Can Type "Q"; This Will Take You Back To This Menu

---

You will then be asked to identify the aquifer type:

1) Confined

2) Unconfined

Enter 1 and < RETURN >.

If your aquifer had been **unconfined**, then your possible choices for adjusting the drawdown in the production well are as follows:

```
1)  Correct for Partial Penetration (Kozeny equation)

2)  Correct for Dewatering of Aquifer

3)  Enter Well Efficiency

4)  No corrections necessary

Choice:  #    < RETURN >

Is this correct (Y/N):  Y    < RETURN >
```

BUT the aquifer **is confined** and your possible choices for adjusting the drawdown in the production well are as follows:

```
1)  Correct for Partial Penetration (Kozeny equation)

2)  Enter Well Efficiency

3)  No corrections necessary

Choice:  3   < RETURN >

Is this correct (Y/N):  Y     < RETURN >
```

Enter 3.

Next, enter in your production well variables:

```
Radius of the well (in feet):  1.0  ◄──────── Remember, this refers to the radius of the
Pumping time (in minutes):  240                production well, not the observation well
Enter pumping rate (in gpm):  500              distance.
Enter drawdown (in feet):  9.65
                                               < RETURN > after each data entry.
Is this correct (Y/N):  Y     < RETURN >
```

Next, you need to either assume a storage coefficient or enter the one you know.

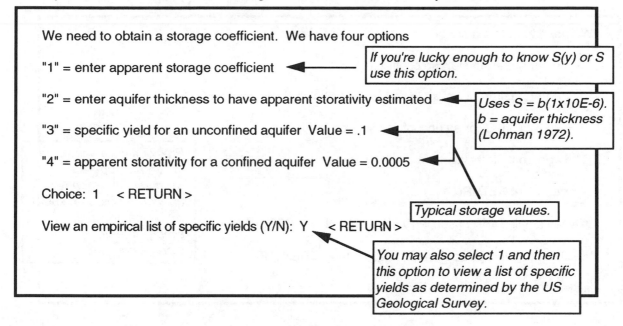

We need to obtain a storage coefficient. We have four options

"1" = enter apparent storage coefficient ◄— *If you're lucky enough to know S(y) or S use this option.*

"2" = enter aquifer thickness to have apparent storativity estimated ◄— *Uses S = b(1x10E-6). b = aquifer thickness (Lohman 1972).*

"3" = specific yield for an unconfined aquifer Value = .1 ◄—

"4" = apparent storativity for a confined aquifer Value = 0.0005 ◄—

Choice: 1   < RETURN >

Typical storage values.

View an empirical list of specific yields (Y/N): Y   < RETURN >

You may also select 1 and then this option to view a list of specific yields as determined by the US Geological Survey.

A library of <u>average</u> hydraulic values for geologic material is available:

Material	% Nu	% Nr	% Sy	Kv	Kh	Kr
1) Sand, Fine	0.43	0.32	0.33	12.600	N/A	8.17
2) Sand, Medium	0.39	0.35	0.32	45.500	N/A	40.00
3) Sand, Coarse	0.39	0.34	0.27	90.00	N/A	147.00

N/A = Not Applicable
% Nu = percent porosity, undisturbed
% Nr = percent porosity, repacked
% Sy = percent specific yield
Kv = vertical hydraulic conductivity = ft/day
Kh = horizontal hydraulic conductivity = ft/day
Kr = repacked hydraulic conductivity = ft/day

You may observe any number of lists or simply use a specific yield value that you prefer

►Enter # of your choice or 0 for other options: 0   < RETURN >

1) The choice is correct; 2) See Subcategory list again
3) Enter a different preferred coefficient: 3   < RETURN >
Please enter storage coefficient: 0.0002   < RETURN >
Is this correct (Y/ N): Y   < RETURN >

Because we are lucky enough to know the storage coefficient, we do not need the previous 2 menus. We can enter S into the program.

We need to obtain a storage coefficient. We have four options

"1" = enter apparent storage coefficient

"2" = enter aquifer thickness to have apparent storativity estimated

"3" = specific yield for an unconfined aquifer Value = .1

"4" = apparent storativity for a confined aquifer Value = 0.0005

Choice: 1   < RETURN >

View an empirical list of specific yields (Y/N): **N**   < RETURN >

Please enter storage coefficient: 0.000198   < RETURN >

Is this correct (Y/ N): Y   < RETURN >

Previously we answered "Y" to this question. If we enter "N", then we are not offered the USGS list option, instead, simply enter in your storage coefficient.

You will then be asked for a **zero drawdown criterion**, **aquifer thickness**, and if you want a **printout**. The results will then appear on your screen. < RETURN > for a printout if you requested one.

Q = Pumping rate = gpm = 500.00   *Ogden/Theis output*
r = Radius of the pumping well = ft= 1.00
t = time duration of pumping test = 240.00 min = 0.16667 days
$t(o)$ = time of zero drawdown = 0.00000938 min = 0.0000000065 days
slope = ft = 1.30342
Transmissivity = T =101271.75 gpd/ft = 1255.77 sq m/day = 13570.42 sq ft/day
Apparent Storage Coefficient = 0.000198
Aquifer thickness = b = ft = 50.00 ft
Hydraulic conductivity = K = 2025.44 gpd/sq ft = 83.04 m/day = 271.40 ft/day
u for s = 0.0000000219
uW(u) for s = 0.0000003742
Field drawdown = s = ft = 9.65
Field specific capacity = Q/s = gpm/ft = 51.81
Apparent limit of the cone of depression at steady-rate = $r(o)$ = ft = 5057.04
u for $s(o)$ = 2.76630232
W(u) for $s(o)$ = 0.01767395
Zero drawdown criterion = $s(o)$ = ft = 0.0100
Apparent transient limit of the cone of depression = $r(L)$ = ft = 11229.61

Press any key to continue

As you can see the production well results match well with the observation well results.

"Apparent" is used, because the storage coefficient is your predicted value.

168

KASENOW /THEIS SPECIFIC CAPACITY METHOD

The Kasenow/Theis Q/s method works similar to the Ogden/Theis solution. **Enter 5** at the TWG main menu and answer the same set of questions until the following spreadsheet appears on your screen. **Then find the two Q/s values between which your calculated Q/s value can be found.**

#	T gpd/ft	u	W(u)	Q/s gpm/ft
1)	1000	2.2E-06	12.4401	0.70
2)	2000	1.1E-06	13.1332	1.33
3)	3000	7.4E-07	13.5387	1.93
4)	4000	5.6E-07	13.8264	2.52
5)	5000	4.4E-07	14.0495	3.11
6)	6000	3.7E-07	14.2319	3.68
7)	7000	3.2E-07	14.3860	4.25
8)	8000	2.8E-07	14.5195	4.81
9)	9000	2.5E-07	14.6373	5.37
10)	10000	2.2E-07	14.7427	5.92
11)	15000	1.5E-07	15.1482	8.64

1) See rest of list; 2) Estimate transmissivity: 1 < RETURN >

Your Q/s: 51.81

The Q/s value, which may have been adjusted according to your specifications, will appear here. This is the value that you use relative to the list on the left

The Q/s value cannot be interpolated in this section of the list: enter 1 to see another page.

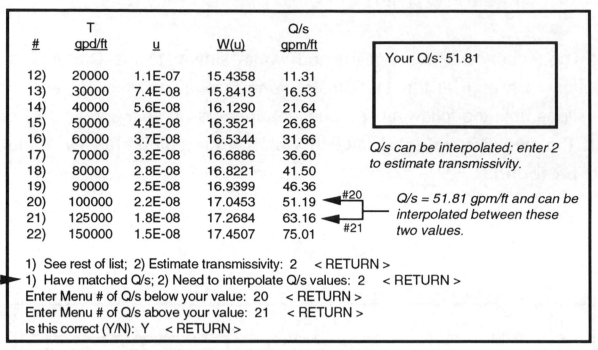

#	T gpd/ft	u	W(u)	Q/s gpm/ft
12)	20000	1.1E-07	15.4358	11.31
13)	30000	7.4E-08	15.8413	16.53
14)	40000	5.6E-08	16.1290	21.64
15)	50000	4.4E-08	16.3521	26.68
16)	60000	3.7E-08	16.5344	31.66
17)	70000	3.2E-08	16.6886	36.60
18)	80000	2.8E-08	16.8221	41.50
19)	90000	2.5E-08	16.9399	46.36
20)	100000	2.2E-08	17.0453	51.19
21)	125000	1.8E-08	17.2684	63.16
22)	150000	1.5E-08	17.4507	75.01

Your Q/s: 51.81

Q/s can be interpolated; enter 2 to estimate transmissivity.

#20
#21

Q/s = 51.81 gpm/ft and can be interpolated between these two values.

1) See rest of list; 2) Estimate transmissivity: 2   < RETURN >
1) Have matched Q/s; 2) Need to interpolate Q/s values: 2   < RETURN >
Enter Menu # of Q/s below your value: 20   < RETURN >
Enter Menu # of Q/s above your value: 21   < RETURN >
Is this correct (Y/N): Y   < RETURN >

Number one will rarely happen, you will generally enter 2.

The preliminary results should next appear on your screen:

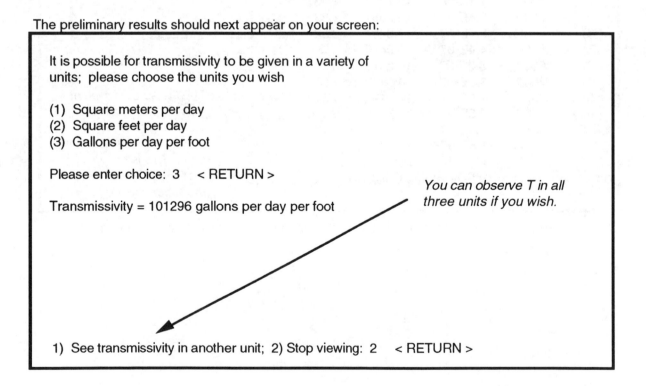

It is possible for transmissivity to be given in a variety of
units; please choose the units you wish

(1) Square meters per day
(2) Square feet per day
(3) Gallons per day per foot

Please enter choice: 3   < RETURN >

Transmissivity = 101296 gallons per day per foot

You can observe T in all three units if you wish.

1) See transmissivity in another unit; 2) Stop viewing: 2   < RETURN >

Again, you will be asked for a **zero drawdown criterion**, **aquifer thickness**, and if you want a **printout**. The results will then appear on your screen. < RETURN > for a printout if you requested one.

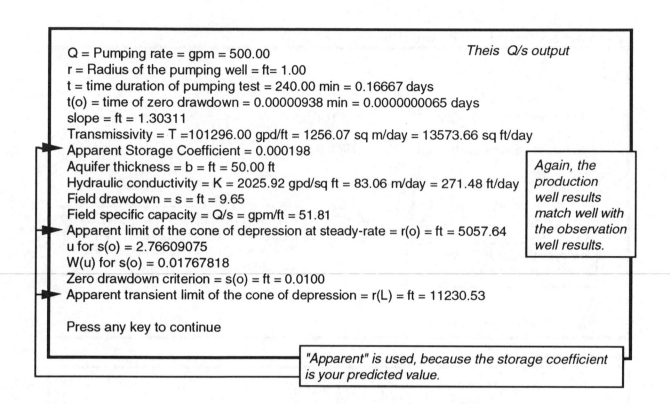

Q = Pumping rate = gpm = 500.00   *Theis Q/s output*
r = Radius of the pumping well = ft= 1.00
t = time duration of pumping test = 240.00 min = 0.16667 days
t(o) = time of zero drawdown = 0.00000938 min = 0.0000000065 days
slope = ft = 1.30311
Transmissivity = T =101296.00 gpd/ft = 1256.07 sq m/day = 13573.66 sq ft/day
Apparent Storage Coefficient = 0.000198
Aquifer thickness = b = ft = 50.00 ft
Hydraulic conductivity = K = 2025.92 gpd/sq ft = 83.06 m/day = 271.48 ft/day
Field drawdown = s = ft = 9.65
Field specific capacity = Q/s = gpm/ft = 51.81
Apparent limit of the cone of depression at steady-rate = r(o) = ft = 5057.64
u for s(o) = 2.76609075
W(u) for s(o) = 0.01767818
Zero drawdown criterion = s(o) = ft = 0.0100
Apparent transient limit of the cone of depression = r(L) = ft = 11230.53

Press any key to continue

Again, the production well results match well with the observation well results.

"Apparent" is used, because the storage coefficient is your predicted value.

You will again be transferred back to the TWG main menu.

DETERMINING TRANSMISSIVITY FROM A STEP-DRAWDOWN TEST

Step-drawdown data on pages 113 and 115 will be used to demonstrate this module. Enter 6 at the TWG main menu. The opening screen should look like the one below:

Enter the drawdown value at the end of the first step.

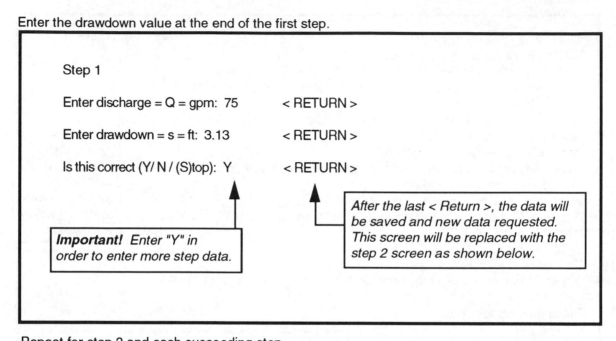

Repeat for step 2 and each succeeding step...

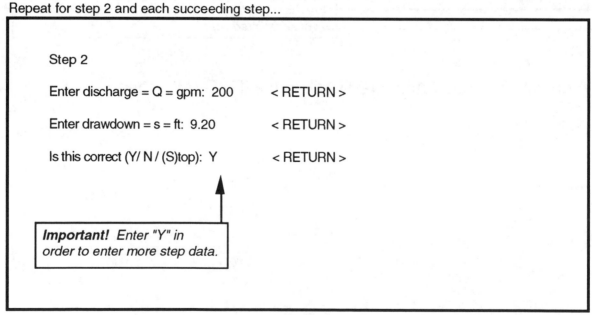

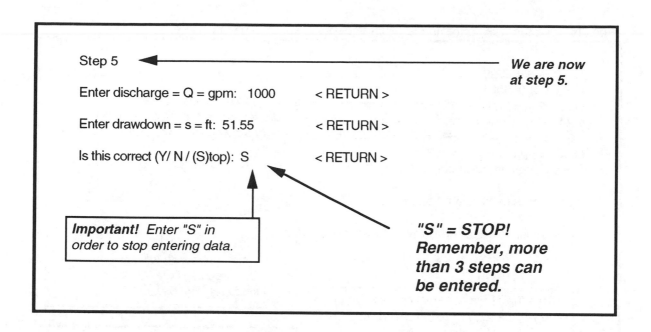

Step 5 ← ——————————————————————— **We are now at step 5.**

Enter discharge = Q = gpm: 1000   < RETURN >

Enter drawdown = s = ft: 51.55   < RETURN >

Is this correct (Y/ N / (S)top): S   < RETURN >

Important! Enter "S" in order to stop entering data.

"S" = STOP! Remember, more than 3 steps can be entered.

You will then be asked for a predicted discharge (in order to utilize the step-drawdown results).

Enter predicted discharge = Q = gpm: 75   < RETURN >

Do you wish to print out results (Y / N): Y   < RETURN >

Is this correct (Y / N): Y

IMPORTANT! *You can use any Q value to predict Q/s using the well performance equations, but you will only be allowed **to calculate transmissivity** when the Q value you wish to predict is equal to the Q value of the first step interval.*

173

Results using the well performance equations should appear on your screen.

B = 0.043185729
C = 0.000009881
s(a) = ft = 3.23893 ◄───────────────────── *drawdown in the aquifer*
s(w) = ft = 0.05558 ◄───────────────────── *drawdown in the production well*
s(t) = ft = 3.29451 ◄───────────────────── *total drawdown in the production well*
Q/s(t) = gpm/ft = 22.76513
R = Correlation coefficient = 0.89542

Do you wish to calculate transmissivity (Y/N): Y ◄   < RETURN >

Do you wish to adjust drawdowns for well loss (Y/N): Y   < RETURN >

This option will only appear when the predicted Q = Q value of the first step interval.

When the Theis assumptions are working and well loss is not extreme, this option will refine the calculated T value.

The next series of questions will be similar to the Theis time-drawdown module.

The aquifer is suspected of being

1) Confined

2) Unconfined

Choice: 1   < RETURN >

174

1) Interpolate drawdowns in Z(u) method

2) Do not interpolate drawdowns

Choice: 2   < RETURN >

Enter time duration of first step interval = t = min: 120

Enter pumping well radius = r(p) = ft (1.0 is default): 0.5

Is this correct (Y/N): Y

< RETURN > after each entry.

(O)pen an existing file or (M)ake new file: M   < RETURN >

Name of save file (up to 8 letters): Confined   < RETURN >

NOTE: All drawdowns from the 1st step interval must be
entered (and only from the 1st interval).

Please press any key to continue

Enter in the drawdowns from the first step interval, then enter F.

#	Time	Drawdown
1)	10.00	2.66
2)	15.00	2.74
3)	20.00	2.79
4)	25.00	2.83
5)	35.00	2.90
6)	40.00	2.92
7)	50.00	2.97
8)	60.00	3.00
9)	70.00	3.03
10)	80.00	3.05
11)	90.00	3.08
12)	100.00	3.10
13)	120.00	3.13

(A)dd; (D)elete; (M)odify one; (F)inished; (R)est of list: F   < RETURN >

The results for the Z(u) method will be displayed on your screen:

t min	s ft	Z(u)	u	W(u)	T gpd/ft
20	2.73	0.9525	2.6E-07	14.580	45828
40	2.86	0.9546	1.3E-07	15.273	45828
50	2.91	0.9520	3.0E-07	14.429	42554
70	2.97	0.9563	7.4E-08	15.847	45793
80	2.99	0.9566	6.6E-08	15.951	45784
100	3.04	0.9573	5.0E-08	16.233	45828
120	3.07	0.9577	4.3E-08	16.392	45828

Average ==>   45349

Remember, if you need to remove anomalous values --- **use the interval.**

Press any key to continue

---

t min	s ft	Z(u)	u	W(u)	T gpd/ft
20	2.73	0.9525	2.6E-07	14.580	45828
40	2.86	0.9546	1.3E-07	15.273	45828
50	2.91	0.9520	3.0E-07	14.429	42554
70	2.97	0.9563	7.4E-08	15.847	45793
80	2.99	0.9566	6.6E-08	15.951	45784
100	3.04	0.9573	5.0E-08	16.233	45828
120	3.07	0.9577	4.3E-08	16.392	45828

Average ==>   45349

Do you wish to look at particular intervals (Y/N): Y   < RETURN >
Do you wish to see list again (Y/N): N   < RETURN >
Do you wish to return to the editor (Y/N): N   < RETURN >

Next, the following questions will be asked:

Do you want to print results?

Do you know aquifer thickness in feet?

After answering the above questions carefully, the results should appear:

```
Q = pumping rate = 75 gpm
Aquifer thickness = 90.00 ft
t = time duration of pumping test = 120.00 min = 0.08333 days
Slope = 0.44 ft
Transmissivity = T = 45348.74 gpd/ft = 6076.73 sq ft / day = 562.32 sq m /day
Hydraulic conductivity = K = 503.87 gpd/sq ft = 67.52 ft / day = 20.66 m /day

Press return when done
```

After pressing return a printout will be delivered if so requested

```
Do you wish to re-calculate with a new Q (Y/N): N



                                    At this point you will be given the option to
                                    predict another specific capacity (Q/s) for any
                                    Q value.  You can do this as often as you like,
                                    but you can only calculate transmissivity when
                                    Q predicted = Q interval.
```

When answering "N" above, you will be taken back to the TWG main menu.

MODELING A PUMP TEST

There are many reasons to model a pump test. The researcher may only have cost effective estimates for T and S (Kasenow, 1993), and cannot afford to actually construct and run a real test: the model itself is cost effective. The investigator can use the model for pump test design --- that is --- test the model to see where the observation wells should be constructed. TWG offers a powerful pump test model that is easy to use.

The pump test model in TWG is based upon the Theis equations, which, theoretically, can be used at any time during a pump test when the Theis assumptions are valid. The model uses a binary search to find and interpolate the best possible u and W(u) values for every value of time entered in the model. Drawdowns are calculated and displayed for up to four observation well distances (r # 1 is always the production well). The limits of predicted data points you are allowed to model are as follows:

4 observation wells = 40 data points
3 observation wells = 50 data points
2 observation wells = 66 data points.

For our example the model will simulate the famous Gridley pump test (Walton, 1962): The Gridley constants and results are as follows: Q = 220 gpm, r = 824 ft, T = 10,100 gpd / ft and S = 0.00002. The drawdowns collected during the Gridley test are displayed below. Compare the Gridley pump test drawdowns to the Gridley model drawdowns and you will find that the model offers good accuracy.

GRIDLEY PUMP TEST DATA	
Q = 220 gpm r = 824 ft T = 10,100 gpd/ft S = 0.00002	
TIME (min)	**s (feet)**
3	0.3
5	0.7
8	1.2
12	2.1
20	3.2
24	3.6
30	4.1
38	4.7
47	5.1
50	5.3
60	5.7
70	6.1
80	6.3
90	6.7
100	7.0
130	7.5
160	8.3
200	8.5
260	9.2
320	9.7
380	10.2
500	10.9

In order to model a pump test enter 7 at the TWG main menu:

THEIS WITHOUT GRAPHS

Please Select A Method For Estimating Aquifer Parameters

1) Theis Time-Drawdown

2) Theis Distance-Drawdown

3) Theis Recovery

4) Ogden / Theis Solution

5) Kasenow / Theis Solution

6) Step-Drawdown Analysis

7) Model a pump test

8) Exit

At Any Menu Option You Can Type "Q"; This Will Take You Back To This Menu

Please enter menu option: 7   < RETURN >

Next, enter the constants for the pump test you wish to model:

< RETURN > after each data entry.

Enter Discharge = Q = gpm: 220
Enter Transmissivity = T = gpd / ft: 10,100
Enter radius of Well #1, the pumping well (Default = 1): 1
Enter Storativity = S: .00002

Is this correct (Y / N): Y   < RETURN >

Do you want a print out of the pump test simulation (Y/ N): Y   < RETURN >

You are able to simulate a pump test for up to 5 wells. Well #1 will always be the production well. Wells 2,3,4,and 5 are observation wells.

181

The next menu should ask for the observation well distances.

You can enter up to 5 observation wells. The pumping well is
observation well #1. Enter up to 4 more observation wells.

Observation well #2 of 5

Enter well distance = ft: 824   < RETURN >

Is this correct (Y/N/(S)top): S   < RETURN > ◄—

*If you wish to enter more than one
observation well, enter "Y". If you
make a mistake, enter "N". Enter "S"
to stop at the current number of
observation wells.*

You will now be asked to enter the times of the desired
drawdowns. In order to operate the editor you must enter
the rank of the time into the drawdown column: 1,2,3,4,...

◄— *This will be
demonstrated
in a moment.*

Press any key to continue

At the editor (M)ake a file

(O)pen an existing file or (M)ake new file: M   < RETURN >

Name of save file (up to 8 letters): Gridsim   < RETURN >

When you are in the editor, enter the data like we have below to model a pump test.

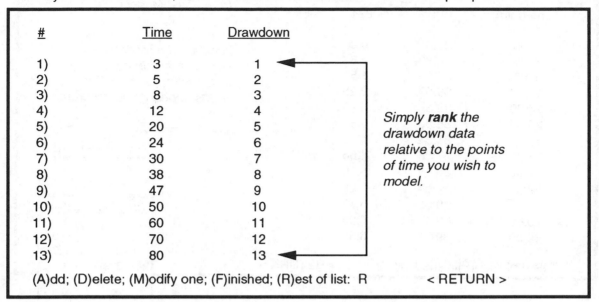

#	Time	Drawdown
1)	3	1
2)	5	2
3)	8	3
4)	12	4
5)	20	5
6)	24	6
7)	30	7
8)	38	8
9)	47	9
10)	50	10
11)	60	11
12)	70	12
13)	80	13

*Simply **rank** the drawdown data relative to the points of time you wish to model.*

(A)dd; (D)elete; (M)odify one; (F)inished; (R)est of list: R   < RETURN >

The second page of your data file should look like this:

#	Time	Drawdown
14)	90	14
15)	100	15
16)	130	16
17)	160	17
18)	200	18
19)	260	19
20)	320	20
21)	380	21
22)	500	22

(A)dd; (D)elete; (M)odify one; (F)inished; (R)est of list: F   < RETURN >

After the data file is completed enter F for the calculations to begin...a few seconds will pass...

Time (min)	1.00 ft	824 ft		Pump Test Model Output

Time (min)	1.00 ft	824 ft
3.00	31.61	0.39
5.00	32.89	0.89
8.00	34.06	1.55
12.00	35.07	2.25
20.00	36.35	3.26
24.00	36.80	3.64
30.00	37.36	4.13
38.00	37.95	4.66
47.00	38.48	5.15
50.00	38.64	5.29
60.00	39.09	5.72
70.00	39.47	6.08
80.00	39.81	6.40

Compare the model output to the actual pump test data collected in the field. The results appear to be accurate.

Observation well distance(s).

GRIDLEY PUMP TEST DATA

Q = 220 gpn
r = 824 ft

TIME (min)	s (feet)
3	0.3
5	0.7
8	1.2
12	2.1
20	3.2
24	3.6
30	4.1
38	4.7
47	5.1
50	5.3
60	5.7
70	6.1
80	6.3
90	6.7
100	7.0
130	7.5
160	8.3
200	8.5
260	9.2
320	9.7
380	10.2
500	10.9

(R)est of list; (F)inished: R   < RETURN >

Time (min)	1.00 ft	824 ft
90.00	40.10	6.68
100.00	40.36	6.93
130.00	41.02	7.57
160.00	41.54	8.07
200.00	42.09	8.62
260.00	42.75	9.26
320.00	43.27	9.78
380.00	43.70	10.20
500.00	44.38	10.88

(R)est of list; (F)inished: F   < RETURN >

Simulate more wells with same input and different distances (Y/N): N   < RETURN >

Do you want to print results (Y/N): Y   < RETURN >

This printout refers to the final printout that displays aquifer and well hydraulic characteristics.

Next, enter the aquifer thickness, if you know it...

Do you know the aquifer thickness in feet (Y/N): Y   < RETURN >

The aquifer thickness = b = ft: 18   < RETURN >

Is this correct (Y/N): Y   < RETURN >

This question is asked in order to calculate hydraulic conductivity from transmissivity using the following formula:

$K = T/b$ *where K = hydraulic conductivity.*

If you don't know the aquifer thickness, the program ignores this calculation.

...then enter your zero drawdown criterion...

If you assume 0.01 feet you must enter it here.

Do you want to estimate r(L), the real limit of the cone of depression using a zero drawdown criterion (Y/N): Y

The real limit = the transient limit; estimated using the Theis equations

Enter zero drawdown criterion (0.01 default) = s(o) = ft: 0.01   < RETURN >

Is this correct (Y/N):   < RETURN >

It should be obvious when examining the Theis equations that a limiting drawdown criterion is needed:

For Consistent Units $s \neq 0$

$$W(u) = \frac{T4\pi s}{Q}$$

$$r_L = \sqrt{\frac{4Ttu}{S}}$$

After W(u) has been determined, a binary search by the computer finds and interpolates the best possible u value within a table similar to that in Appendix A.

185

The TWG output is displayed on the screen.

```
Q = pumping rate = 220.00 gpm                              Pump Test Model Output
Aquifer thickness = 18.00 ft
t = time duration of pumping test = 500.00 min = 0.34722 days
Slope = 5.75 ft
Transmissivity = T =10100.00 gpd/ft = 1353.40 sq ft/day = 125.24  sq m/day
Hydraulic conductivity = K = 561.11 gpd/sq ft = 75.19 ft/day = 23.01 m/day
S = Storativity = 0.00002
r(o) = limit of the cone of depression at steady-rate = 7252.87 ft
s(o) = zero drawdown criterion = ft = 0.01
r(L) = transient limit of the cone of depression = ft = 19363.92
W(u) for s(o) = dimensionless = 0.00401
u for s(o) = dimensionless = 3.99879
s(p) = drawdown in the pumping well at 100% efficiency = 44.38 ft
Q/s = Specific capacity of pumping well at 100% efficiency = 4.96 gpm/ft


Press return when done
```

After pressing return, a printout with the same information is released...(if requested)...and you will return to the TWG main menu.

RUN TIME ERRORS

TWG HAS BEEN EXTENSIVELY TESTED by competent hydrogeology students and engineers. We do not anticipate any major problems, but all computer programs have "bugs" that crop up, especially when users do the unexpected. If this occurs, please tell us about the problem and we'll fix it and replace your copy.

If "Runtime Errors" occur please review the list below for possible explanations:

Runtime Error 101: This is a disk write error. Your disk is probably full and has no available memory. Use a new disk.

Runtime Error 150: Disk is write protected. Check your disk.

Runtime Error 159: Printer is probably out of paper.

Runtime Error 160: This is a device write fault error. Hopefully your printer is not turned on. If your printer is turned on then this may be a hard-drive problem.

Runtime Error 200: Division by zero. Check your data input. Do not add a zero drawdown or a zero time into any editor.

Runtime Error 205: These are floating point errors. The number is too and 206 big (205) or too small (206) for the computer to compute. Safety features written into APE should prevent these errors from occurring.

NINE

ADDITIONAL PUMP TEST EXAMPLES

PUMP TEST DATA

Pump test data on the following pages assumes that drawdown is in harmony with the Theis assumptions. Following is a review of the Theis assumptions:

1) Discharge from the pumping well is instantaneous with decline in pressure.
2) The well fully penetrates and is open through the entire extent of the aquifer.
3) The well's radius is very small so that well storage is negligible.
4) Flow to the well screen is radial, horizontal and laminar.
5) The aquifer is homogeneous and isotropic.
6) Aquifer thickness is uniform.
7) The aquifer remains saturated during the entire pumping test.
8) The aquifer is infinite (in areal extent, no areal boundaries).
9) The aquifer is horizontal and bounded above and below by impermeable beds (aquifer is confined).
10) All storage of water within the aquifer comes from the cone of depression (the aquifer is isolated from overlying or underlying leaky aquifers, local recharge, precipitation, irrigation, rivers, lakes and wetlands).

Regarding the data sets you have used or are about to use: some of your T and S values may differ from the expected results when you use the TWG interval to refine your data base, but a good match should occur.

For those of you who prefer to hack your way through the TWG program, and who have given this book a quick reading, please be aware that pump test data can also be found on the following pages:

unconfined specific capacity data on page 37

unconfined recovery data on page 53;

confined recovery data on page 54;

confined boundary conditions on page 85;

Step-drawdown data on page 109;

Step-drawdown data on page 115;

confined specific capacity data on page 127;

confined pump test data on page 141;

confined pump test data on page 150; and

confined pump test data on page 180.

PROBLEMS 1 AND 2

If you have utilized the above data sets, then hopefully you have gained experience and confidence in using the Theis Without Graphs computer program. Pump test data for problems 1 and 2, in this section, are for confined aquifers. Problem 1 is a time-drawdown data set; problem 2 can be used in either the time-drawdown or distance drawdown TWG modules. Your transmissivity and storativity values for problem 1 should be about 61,639 gpd/ft and 0.00012, respectively. The T and S values for problem 2, using either time or distance-drawdown methods, should be about 12,500 gpd/ft and 0.0004, respectively.

Problem 1: Time-Drawdown: Aquifer Type: Confined

Q = 300 gpm   Results:
r = 150 ft   T = 61,639 gpd/ft
b = 120 ft   S = 0.00012

t (min)	s (ft)
1.00	0.94
1.50	1.14
2.00	1.29
2.50	1.41
3.00	1.51
4.00	1.66
5.00	1.79
6.00	1.89
8.00	2.04
10.00	2.17
12.00	2.27
14.00	2.35
18.00	2.49
24.00	2.65
30.00	2.78
40.00	2.94
50.00	3.06
60.00	3.16
80.00	3.32
100.00	3.45
120.00	3.55
150.00	3.68
180.00	3.78
210.00	3.86
240.00	3.94
300.00	4.06

Problem 2: Confined

Q = 200 gpm

r = 200 ft, 400 ft, 800 ft and 1000 ft

b = 20 ft

T = 12,500 gpd/ft

S = 0.000040

t (min)	s (ft): 200 ft	s (ft): 400 ft	s(ft): 800 ft	s(ft): 1000 ft
1.00	1.48	0.22	0.00	0.00
2.00	2.47	0.70	0.03	0.01
3.00	3.12	1.12	0.11	0.03
4.00	3.59	1.48	0.22	0.07
5.00	3.97	1.78	0.34	0.13
6.00	4.28	2.04	0.46	0.20
8.00	4.79	2.47	0.70	0.35
10.00	5.18	2.82	0.92	0.51
12.00	5.50	3.12	1.12	0.66
20.00	6.42	3.97	1.78	1.20
24.00	6.75	4.28	2.04	1.42
30.00	7.15	4.67	2.37	1.72
40.00	7.67	5.18	2.82	2.13
50.00	8.08	5.58	3.18	2.47
60.00	8.41	5.90	3.48	2.76
70.00	8.69	6.18	3.74	3.00
80.00	8.94	6.42	3.97	3.22
90.00	9.15	6.63	4.17	3.41
100.00	9.35	6.82	4.35	4.04
130.00	9.82	7.30	4.81	3.59
160.00	10.20	7.67	5.18	4.04
200.00	10.61	8.08	5.58	4.79
250.00	11.02	8.49	5.98	5.18
300.00	11.36	8.82	6.30	5.50
320.00	11.47	8.94	6.42	5.62
380.00	11.79	9.25	6.73	5.93
500.00	12.29	9.75	7.23	6.42
600.00	12.63	10.09	7.56	6.75

PROBLEM 3

Problem three contains pump test drawdown data for a water table aquifer with no delayed yield (Ground Water Manual, 1981). Drawdown needs to be corrected for dewatering using equation (5). The reported values from the *Ground Water Manual* using the Cooper-Jacob time-drawdown method are about 154,000 and 0.23 for transmissivity and specific yield, respectively. Values of T and S obtained using distance-drawdown data (extended data not found in *Ground Water Manual*) are about 150,000 gpd/ft and .24, respectively. When Theis curves for time and distance-drawdown are used, values calculated for T and S are about 150,000 gpd/ft and .24, respectively.

<u>Problem 3</u>: Aquifer Type: Unconfined: Uncorrected Drawdowns

Q = 1162.64 gpm   T = 150,000 gpd/ft

r = 30 ft, 60 ft, 120 ft   S = 0.24

b = 26 ft

t (min)	s (ft): 30 ft	s (ft): 60 ft	s(ft): 120 ft
2.00	0.04	0.00	0.00
4.00	0.19	0.00	0.00
6.00	0.35	0.02	0.00
8.00	0.51	0.04	0.00
10.00	0.63	0.08	0.00
15.00	0.90	0.17	0.00
20.00	1.11	0.27	0.01
25.00	1.28	0.38	0.02
30.00	1.43	0.47	0.04
35.00	1.56	0.55	0.05
40.00	1.67	0.63	0.07
45.00	1.77	0.68	0.10
50.00	1.86	0.76	0.12
55.00	1.94	0.84	0.15
60.00	2.02	0.90	0.18
70.00	2.16	1.00	0.21
80.00	2.28	1.11	0.27
90.00	2.40	1.20	0.32
100.00	2.50	1.28	0.37
110.00	2.59	1.36	0.43
120.00	2.67	1.42	0.47
150.00	2.88	1.61	0.60
180.00	3.06	1.77	0.70
210.00	3.21	1.91	0.81
240.00	3.35	2.02	0.90

PROBLEM 4

Problem four contains residual drawdown recovery data for an observation well screened in a confined aquifer. The data is related to the Lohman (1972) time-drawdown data for an observation well at r = 200 ft. If you have been using the Lohman data to learn TWG, then you are aware that T and S values for the Theis time-drawdown method are about 101,000 gpd/ft and 0.0002, respectively; and about 100,000 gpd/ft and 0.0002 for distance-drawdown, respectively.

Problem 4: Time-Drawdown: Observation Well Recovery Data

Q = 500 gpm   Results:

r = 200 ft   T = 101,050 gpd/ft

S_{off} = 3.67 ft   S = 0.00019

t = 240 min

t' (min)	s' (ft)
2.00	2.66
3.00	2.49
5.00	2.23
7.00	2.10
10.00	1.84
15.00	1.61
20.00	1.48
30.00	1.25
40.00	1.12
60.00	0.92
80.00	0.79
100.00	0.69
140.00	0.56
180.00	0.46
200.00	0.45
220.00	0.42
240.00	0.39

PROBLEM 5

Problem five contains pump test drawdown data and residual drawdown recovery data for an observation well screened in a water table aquifer with no delayed yield (Ground Water Manual, 1981). Drawdowns **have been** corrected for dewatering. Reported values from the *Ground Water Manual* for this system, using residual drawdown data, range from 341,447 to 345,755 gpd/ft for transmissivity, and 0.07 for specific yield. When observation well pump test data are used with the Theis time-drawdown curve, calculated T and S values are about 347,000 gpd/ft and 0.65, respectively.

Problem 5: Aquifer Type: Unconfined: Corrected Drawdowns
Pump Test and Recovery: Observation Well

Q = 1218.5 gpm T_{pt} = 347,742 gpd/ft, T_{rec} = 344,326 gpd/ft

r = 100 ft S_{pt} = 0.065, S_{rec} = 0.059

t (min)	s (ft): ft	t' (min)	s' (ft): ft
10	0.22	5	1.78
15	0.33	10	1.64
20	0.41	15	1.53
25	0.50	20	1.45
30	0.55	25	1.37
40	0.66	30	1.32
50	0.73	40	1.22
60	0.80	50	1.15
70	0.86	60	1.09
80	0.92	70	1.03
90	0.96	80	0.97
100	1.00	90	0.94
110	1.04	100	0.90
120	1.07	110	0.87
180	1.24	120	0.85
240	1.35	180	0.70
300	1.45	240	0.61
360	1.52	300	0.54
420	1.59	360	0.49
480	1.65	420	0.46
540	1.71	480	0.40
600	1.73	600	0.36
660	1.77	660	0.34
720	1.81	720	0.31
800	1.86	800	0.29

PROBLEM 6

Problem 6 contains step-drawdown data which was obtained from pump test analysis of a confined aquifer in southeast Michigan. The transmissivity was determined to be about 54,000 gpd / ft and the storage coefficient about 0.0004. The resulting transmissivity from the step-drawdown test, utilizing the TWG program, is 60,050 gpd/ft before refinement of drawdowns and 59,112 gpd/ft after refinement. Either one of these values would have been a reasonable estimate of the aquifer's transmissivity if it were not economically feasible to conduct a full scale pump test. To obtain these results, the TWG interval was used from 30 to 120 minutes with no interpolation of drawdown data. Interpolating drawdown data and using the same interval results in a transmissivity of 61,641 gpd/ft --- still a reasonable estimate of the aquifer's transmissivity.

Problem 6: Step-Drawdown Test

$$r_w = 0.50 \text{ ft}$$

T at step 1 interval 30 to 120 minutes = 59,112 gpd/ft

	Step 1	Step 2	Step 3
	Q = 275 gpm	Q = 540 gpm	Q = 820 gpm
t (min)	s (ft)	s (ft)	s (ft)
5.00	-----	------	26.48
7.00	4.51	------	------
10.00	4.46	11.36	31.74
15.00	4.43	------	31.90
20.00	4.57	11.46	32.29
25.00	4.66	11.81	------
30.00	4.77	12.56	32.47
40.00	4.95	12.81	32.80
50.00	5.01	13.00	32.91
60.00	5.11	13.34	33.16
75.00	5.21	13.49	33.32
90.00	5.29	13.69	33.48
105.00	5.42	13.77	33.63
120.00	5.53	13.89	33.73

Problem seven contains pump test drawdown data and residual drawdown recovery data for an observation well screened in a confined aquifer (Bruin and Hudson, 1955).

Problem six offers another demonstration of the accuracy of the Z(u) method when utilizing intervals. From about 8 minutes to about 193 minutes consistent values of T and S are about 283,403 gpd/ft and 0.000308, respectively, when analyzing pump test data. At about 313 minutes to about 1773 minutes T and S pump test values abruptly change, but in a **consistent** manner, and are estimated to be about 395,267 gpd/ft and 0.000179, respectively. The **consistent** change in these important aquifer parameters offers evidence that the cone of depression has crossed into different sedimentary material. When the two T and S values are averaged, they are reported to be about 333,742 gpd/ft and 0.000250, respectively. Residual drawdown recovery data confirms these results: T = 333,655 gpd/ft and S = 0.00030.

Problem 7: Aquifer Type: Unconfined: Corrected Drawdowns
Pump Test and Recovery: Observation Well

Q = 1770 gpm T_{pt} = 333,742 gpd/ft, T_{rec} = 333,665 gpd/ft

r = 1270 ft S_{pt} = 0.00025, S_{rec} = 0.00030

t (min)	s (ft): ft	t (min)	s(ft): ft
4.00	0.10	313.00	2.37
5.00	0.15	373.00	2.45
6.00	0.21	433.00	2.54
7.00	0.26	493.00	2.59
8.00	0.32	583.00	2.69
9.00	0.37	643.00	2.75
10.00	0.41	703.00	2.79
12.00	0.50	763.00	2.82
14.00	0.57	823.00	2.86
16.00	0.64	943.00	2.94
18.00	0.71	1003.00	2.96
20.00	0.78	1063.00	2.98
23.00	0.86	1123.00	3.00
26.00	0.94	1183.00	3.04
29.00	1.00	1243.00	3.06
32.00	1.05	1303.00	3.20
36.00	1.12	1363.00	3.12
41.00	1.18	1773.00	3.43
46.00	1.25		
51.00	1.31		
61.00	1.42		
66.00	1.47		
103.00	1.76		
133.00	1.93		
163.00	2.04		
193.00	2.16		

t' (min)	s' (ft): ft
1.5	3.42
3.0	3.36
4.0	3.30
5.0	3.24
7.0	3.13
9.0	3.05
13.0	2.89
17.0	2.77
21.0	2.64
28.0	2.48
43.0	2.35
73.0	2.01
103.0	1.82
163.0	1.54
283.0	1.27
403.0	1.12
523.0	1.02
643.0	0.92
763.0	0.83
883.0	0.78
963.0	0.73

Pump Test Project

The pump test project contains pump test drawdown data and residual drawdown recovery data for a production well and three observation wells screened in a confined aquifer. Residual drawdown data for the third observation well is not available. Transmissivity (T), storativity (S), and the real limit of the cone of depression (r_L = transient limit) have been determined using the TWG program. The limiting drawdown criterion (s_o) used to calculate the transient limit of the cone of depression is 0.01 ft. Production well radius was assumed to be 1.0 ft in order to estimate drawdown in the production well at 100% well efficiency. Results are compiled below:

Time-Drawdown

Well	r = ft	Method	T = gpd /ft	S = dim	r_L = ft
pw	---	recovery	51,410	---	---
Obs 1	50	pump test	52,487	0.0018	5710
Obs 1	50	recovery	52,298	0.0019	5499
Obs 2	120	pump test	51,502	0.0021	5255
Obs 2	120	recovery	52,355	0.0020	5400
Obs 3	200	pump test	53,591	0.0017	5937

Distance Drawdown

Obs 1, 2, and 3

Time = 900 min	pump test	52,385	0.0018	5578
	mean	52,290	0.0019	5563

Resulting transmissivity using production well pump test data is 45,707 gpd/ft. Comparing this value to the mean T value calculated from observation well data indicates a well efficiency less than 100% relative to the production well. The drawdown in the production well at 900 minutes was 22.67 feet. The resulting field specific capacity is $Q/s = 540$ gpm $/ 22.67 = 23.82$ gpm/ft. Comparing the field specific capacity and pump test drawdown in the production well to predicted Q/s_p and s_p values, obtained from the TWG program, results in a well efficiency of about 80.5 %:

Time-Drawdown				100% Well Efficiency	
Well	$r = ft$	Method	$T = gpd /ft$	$s_p = ft$	Q/s_p
pw	---	recovery	51,410	---	---
Obs 1	50	pump test	52,487	18.30	29.51
Obs 1	50	recovery	52,298	18.27	29.55
Obs 2	120	pump test	51,502	18.44	29.28
Obs 2	120	recovery	52,355	18.22	29.64
Obs 3	200	pump test	53,591	18.02	29.97

Distance Drawdown
Obs 1, 2, and 3

Time = 900 min		pump test	52,385	18.28	29.54
		mean	52,290	18.26	29.58

Well efficiency (E_w)

mean predicted $s_p \div$ production well $s_w = E_w = 80.5$ %

production well $Q/s \div$ mean predicted $Q/s_p = E_w = 80.5\%$

The calculated well efficiency is reasonable considering that Patchick (1967) and Driscoll (1986) estimate that well efficiency is generally no greater than about 80 to 85 % in production wells that have been properly constructed and developed. Notice that pump test and recovery T values for the production well differ by an error factor of about 11.1%. Transmissivity calculated using residual drawdown and recovery methods is preferable relative to T values calculated using pump test data, especially when evaluating production wells, because during recovery there is no production well turbulence to contend with.

Pump Test Project: Production Well Pump Test

Q = 540 gpm

r_w = 0.05 ft

t = 900 min

Results:

T at interval 28 to 900

minutes = 45,707 gpd/ft

t (min)	s (ft)	t (min)	s (ft)
10.00	16.59	160.00	20.34
11.00	16.71	180.00	20.50
12.00	16.83	200.00	20.64
13.00	16.94	220.00	20.77
14.00	17.04	240.00	20.88
15.00	17.13	260.00	20.99
16.00	17.22	280.00	21.09
17.00	17.30	300.00	21.19
18.00	17.38	330.00	21.31
19.00	17.45	360.00	21.43
20.00	17.52	390.00	21.54
22.00	17.65	420.00	21.64
24.00	17.77	450.00	21.73
26.00	17.88	480.00	21.82
28.00	17.98	540.00	21.98
30.00	18.07	600.00	22.12
35.00	18.28	660.00	22.25
40.00	18.46	720.00	22.37
45.00	18.62	780.00	22.48
50.00	18.76	840.00	22.58
55.00	18.89	900.00	22.67 pump off
60.00	19.01		
70.00	19.22		
80.00	19.40		
90.00	19.56		
100.00	19.70		
110.00	19.83		
120.00	19.95		
140.00	20.15		

Pump Test Project: Recovery Test - Production Well

Q = 540 gpm

Results:

r_w = 0.50 ft

T = 51,410 gpd/ft

t = 900 min

Interval at t' = 4 min to t' = 240 min

t' (min)	s' (ft)	t' (min)	s' (ft)
1.00	6.20	135.00	2.50
3.00	6.18	150.00	2.44
4.00	6.16	165.00	2.34
5.00	6.15	180.00	2.19
6.00	6.00	210.00	1.94
7.00	5.55	240.00	1.83
8.00	5.35		
9.00	5.25		
10.00	5.18		
12.00	5.09		
14.00	4.96		
16.00	4.86		
18.00	4.79		
20.00	4.76		
25.00	4.46		
30.00	4.31		
35.00	4.19		
40.00	3.99		
45.00	3.76		
50.00	3.60		
55.00	3.55		
60.00	3.49		
70.00	3.20		
80.00	3.18		
90.00	3.02		
100.00	2.96		
110.00	2.77		
120.00	2.65		

Pump Test Project: Pump Test - Observation Well 1

Q = 540 gpm   Results:

r = 50 ft   T = 52,448 gpd/ft

t = 900 min   S = 0.0018

t (min)	s (ft)	t (min)	s (ft)
5.00	3.00	720.00	8.80
9.00	3.67	780.00	8.90
15.00	4.26	840.00	8.99
20.00	4.59	900.00	9.07 pump off
25.00	4.85		
30.00	5.07		
40.00	5.40		
50.00	5.66		
60.00	5.88		
75.00	6.14		
90.00	6.36		
105.00	6.54		
120.00	6.69		
140.00	6.88		
160.00	7.03		
200.00	7.30		
220.00	7.41		
240.00	7.51		
270.00	7.65		
300.00	7.77		
330.00	7.88		
360.00	7.99		
396.00	8.10		
420.00	8.17		
450.00	8.25		
480.00	8.33		
540.00	8.46		
600.00	8.59		
660.00	8.70		

Pump Test Project: Recovery Test - Observation Well 1

Q = 540 gpm

r = 50 ft

Interval: 5 min to 240 min

Results:

T = 52,298 gpd/ft

S = 0.0019

t' (min)	s' (ft)	t' (min)	s' (ft)
5.00	5.52	120	2.68
6.00	5.39	135	2.58
7.00	5.31	150	2.37
8.00	5.24	165	2.24
9.00	5.15	180	2.11
10.00	5.08	210	1.89
12.00	4.95	240	1.79
14.00	4.84		
16.00	4.72		
18.00	4.63		
20.00	4.50		
25.00	4.27		
30.00	4.12		
35.00	3.98		
40.00	3.85		
45.00	3.74		
50.00	3.64		
55.00	3.54		
60.00	3.45		
70.00	3.28		
80.00	3.11		
90.00	2.99		
100.00	2.86		
110.00	2.77		

Pump Test Project: Pump Test - Observation Well 2

Q = 540 gpm   <u>Results:</u>

r = 120 ft   T = 51,502 gpd/ft

t = 900 min   S = 0.0021

<u>t (min)</u>	<u>s (ft)</u>	<u>t (min)</u>	<u>s (ft)</u>
2.00	0.38	60.00	3.71
3.00	0.63	70.00	3.89
4.00	0.58	80.00	4.04
5.00	1.04	90.00	4.18
6.00	1.21	100.00	4.31
7.00	1.35	110.00	4.42
8.00	1.48	120.00	4.52
9.00	1.60	140.00	4.71
10.00	1.71	160.00	4.86
11.00	1.80	180.00	5.00
12.00	1.89	200.00	5.13
13.00	1.98	220.00	5.24
14.00	2.06	240.00	5.35
15.00	2.13	260.00	5.44
16.00	2.20	280.00	5.53
17.00	2.27	300.00	5.61
18.00	2.33	330.00	5.73
19.00	2.39	360.00	5.83
20.00	2.45	390.00	5.93
22.00	2.55	420.00	6.02
24.00	2.65	450.00	6.10
26.00	2.74	480.00	6.17
28.00	2.83	540.00	6.32
30.00	2.90	600.00	6.44
35.00	3.08	660.00	6.56
40.00	3.23	720.00	6.66
45.00	3.37	780.00	6.76
50.00	3.49	840.00	6.85
55.00	3.60	900.00	6.93 pump off

Pump Test Project: Recovery Test - Observation Well 2

Q = 540 gpm   Results:

r = 120 ft   T = 52,335 gpd/ft

t = 900 min   S = 0.0020

Interval: t' = 4.00 min to t ' = 240 min

t' (min)	s' (ft)	t' (min)	s' (ft)
1.00	6.37	75.00	3.20
2.00	5.91	80.00	3.16
3.00	5.70	90.00	2.99
4.00	5.56	100.00	2.86
5.00	5.45	110.00	2.77
6.00	5.37	120.00	2.60
7.00	5.28	135.00	2.45
8.00	5.17	150.00	2.35
9.00	5.14	165.00	2.20
10.00	5.04	180.00	2.07
12.00	4.95	210.00	1.88
14.00	4.87	240.00	1.80
16.00	4.77		
18.00	4.59		
20.00	4.54		
22.00	4.49		
24.00	4.39		
26.00	4.32		
28.00	4.27		
30.00	4.19		
35.00	4.03		
40.00	3.93		
45.00	3.75		
50.00	3.67		
55.00	3.58		
60.00	3.47		
65.00	3.36		
70.00	3.32		

Pump Test Project: Pump Test - Observation Well 3

Q = 540 gpm

r = 200 ft

t = 900 min

<u>Results:</u>

T = 53,591 gpd/ft

S = 0.0017

<u>t (min)</u>	<u>s (ft)</u>	<u>t (min)</u>	<u>s (ft)</u>
5.00	0.45	660.00	5.42
10.00	0.94	720.00	5.52
15.00	1.29	740.00	5.56
20.00	1.56	780.00	5.62
25.00	1.79	820.00	5.67
30.00	1.97	840.00	5.70
40.00	2.27	860.00	5.73
50.00	2.51	880.00	5.76
60.00	2.71	900.00	5.78 pump off
70.00	2.88		
80.00	3.03		
90.00	3.16		
100.00	3.28		
110.00	3.38		
120.00	3.48		
140.00	3.65		
160.00	3.80		
200.00	4.06		
220.00	4.17		
240.00	4.27		
270.00	4.40		
300.00	4.52		
330.00	4.63		
360.00	4.73		
380.00	4.79		
420.00	4.91		
450.00	4.98		
480.00	5.06		
540.00	5.19		
600.00	5.32		

REFERENCES

REFERENCES

Ballukraya, P.N., and K.K. Sharma, 1991. Estimation of storativity from recovery data. Ground Water, v.29, n.4

Bardsley, W.E., Sneyd, A.D., and P.D.H. Hill, 1980. An improved method of least-squares parameter estimation with pumping-test data. Journal of Hydrology, v.80.

Berg, A.V., 1975. Determining aquifer coefficients from residual drawdown data. Water Resources Research, v.11, n.6.

Bierschenk, W.H., 1964. Determining well efficiency by multiple step-drawdown tests. International Association of Scientific Hydrology, Publication 64.

Brown, R.H., 1953. Selected procedures for analyzing aquifer test data. Journal of American Water Works Association, v.5, n.8.

Brown, R.H., 1963. Estimating the transmissibility of an artesian aquifer from the specific capacity of a well. USGS Water Supply Paper 1536-I.

Bruin, J., and H.E. Hudson, Jr., 1955. Selected methods for pumping test analysis. Illinois State Water Survey, Report of Investigation Number 25.

Butler, S.S., 1957. Engineering Hydrology. Prentice-Hall, Inc., Englewood Cliffs, New Jersey.

Case, C.M., Pidcoe, W.W., and P.R. Fenske, 1974. Theis equation analysis of residual drawdown data. Water Resources Research, v.10, n.6.

Cooper, H.H., Jr., and C.E. Jacob, 1946. A generalized graphical method for evaluating formation constants and summarizing well-field history. Transactions of the American Geophysical Union, v.27, n.4.

Davis, S.N., and R.J.M. DeWiest, 1966. Hydrogeology. John Wiley and Sons, New York.

Dawson, K.J., and J.D. Istok, 1991. Aquifer Testing. Lewis Publishers, Chelsea, Michigan.

Driscoll, F.G., 1986. Groundwater and Wells. Johnson Division, St. Paul, Minnesota.

Fetter, C.W. , 1988. Applied Hydrogeology, 2nd edition. Macmillan Publishing Company, New York.

Ground Water Manual,1981. See US Department of the Interior, 1981.

Groundwater and Wells, 1986. See Driscoll, F.G.

Heath, R.C., 1987. Basic ground-water hydrology. USGS Water Supply Paper 2220.

Heath, R.C., and F.W. Trainer, 1968. Introduction to Ground Water Hydrology. National Water Well Association, Dublin, Ohio.

Hurr, R.T., 1966. A new approach for estimating transmissibility from specific capacity. Groundwater, v.2,n.4.

Jacob, C.E., 1947. Drawdown test to determine effective radius of artesian well. Transactions, American Society Civil Engineers, v.112.

Jacob, C.E., 1963. Determining the permeability of water-table aquifers. USGS Water Supply Paper 1536-I.

Jacob, C.E., 1963. The recovery method for determining the coefficient of transmissibility. USGS Water Supply Paper 1536-I.

Kasenow, M.C., 1993. Introduction to Aquifer Analysis, 2nd Edition. Wm. C. Brown Publishers, Dubuque, Iowa.

Kruseman, G.P., and N.A. de Ridder, 1990. Analysis and Evaluation of Pumping Test Data. International Institute for Land Reclamation and Improvement, Publication 47. Netherlands.

Lohman, S.W., 1972. Ground-water hydraulics. US Geological Survey Professional Paper 708.

May, H. G., 1963. A simplified time-and distance drawdown graph. US Geological Survey Water Supply Paper 1545-C.

Ogden, L., 1965. Estimating transmissibility with one drawdown. Groundwater, v.3,n.3.

Patchick, P.F., 1967. Predicting well yields - two case histories. Groundwater, v.5,n.2.

Prickett, T.A., 1965. Type-curve solution to aquifer tests under water-table conditions. Groundwater, v.3,n.3.

Sheahan, N.T., 1967. A non-graphical method of determining u and W(u). Ground Water, v.5, n.2.

Theis, C.V., 1935. The relation between the lowering of the piezometric surface and the rate and duration of discharge of a well using ground-water storage. Transactions of the American Geophysical Union, v.16.

Theis, C.V., 1963. Estimating the transmissibility of a water-table aquifer from the specific capacity of a well. US Geological Survey Water Supply Paper 1536-I

Thomasson, H.G., F.H. Olmsted, and E.F. LeRoux, 1960. Geology, water resources and usable ground-water storage capacity of part of Solano County, California. US Geological Survey Water Supply Paper 1464.

Todd, D.K., 1980. Groundwater Hydrology. 2nd edition. John Wiley and Sons, New York.

Turcan, A.N., Jr., 1962. Estimating the specific capacity of a well. US Geological Survey Professional Paper 450-E.

Ulrick and Associates, 1989. Sensitivity Analysis Program - PUMP. Berkeley, California.

US Department of the Interior, 1981. Ground Water Manual. John Wiley and Sons, Inc., New York.

Vanderberg, A., 1975. Program tebes, transmissivity, leakage factor and storativity from a least squares fit of residual drawdown. Department of the Environment, Canada.

Village of Columbiaville, Michigan, 1989. Pump test data. Columbia, Michigan.

Village of Dexter, Michigan, 1991. Pump test data. Dexter, Michigan.

Village of Pinckney, Michigan, 1990. Pump test data. Pinckney, Michigan.

Walton, W.C., 1962. Selected analytical methods for well and aquifer evaluation. Bulletin 49, Illinois State Water Survey.

Walton, W.C., 1988. Groundwater Pumping Tests. Lewis Publishers, Chelsea, Michigan.

Wenzel, L.K., 1942. Methods for determining permeability of water-bearing materials. US Geological Survey Water-Supply Paper 887.

INDEX

INDEX

225

<u>APPENDICES</u>

APPENDIX A

TABLE OF u, W(u), uW(u) and Z(u)

VALUES OF u, W(u), uW(u) and Z(u)

u	W(u)	uW(u)	Z(u)
1.0000E-10	2.2450E+01	2.2450E-09	9.6912E-01
1.1000E-10	2.2350E+01	2.4585E-09	9.6899E-01
1.2000E-10	2.2270E+01	2.6724E-09	9.6887E-01
1.3000E-10	2.2190E+01	2.8847E-09	9.6876E-01
1.4000E-10	2.2110E+01	3.0954E-09	9.6865E-01
1.5000E-10	2.2040E+01	3.3060E-09	9.6856E-01
1.6000E-10	2.1980E+01	3.5168E-09	9.6846E-01
1.7000E-10	2.1920E+01	3.7264E-09	9.6838E-01
1.8000E-10	2.1860E+01	3.9348E-09	9.6829E-01
1.9000E-10	2.1810E+01	4.1439E-09	9.6821E-01
2.0000E-10	2.1760E+01	4.3520E-09	9.6814E-01
2.1000E-10	2.1710E+01	4.5591E-09	9.6807E-01
2.2000E-10	2.1660E+01	4.7652E-09	9.6800E-01
2.3000E-10	2.1620E+01	4.9726E-09	9.6793E-01
2.4000E-10	2.1570E+01	5.1768E-09	9.6787E-01
2.5000E-10	2.1530E+01	5.3825E-09	9.6781E-01
2.6000E-10	2.1490E+01	5.5874E-09	9.6775E-01
2.7000E-10	2.1460E+01	5.7942E-09	9.6769E-01
2.8000E-10	2.1420E+01	5.9976E-09	9.6764E-01
2.9000E-10	2.1380E+01	6.2002E-09	9.6759E-01
3.0000E-10	2.1350E+01	6.4050E-09	9.6753E-01
3.1000E-10	2.1320E+01	6.6092E-09	9.6748E-01
3.2000E-10	2.1290E+01	6.8128E-09	9.6744E-01
3.3000E-10	2.1250E+01	7.0125E-09	9.6739E-01
3.4000E-10	2.1220E+01	7.2148E-09	9.6734E-01
3.5000E-10	2.1200E+01	7.4200E-09	9.6730E-01
3.6000E-10	2.1170E+01	7.6212E-09	9.6725E-01
3.7000E-10	2.1140E+01	7.8218E-09	9.6721E-01
3.8000E-10	2.1110E+01	8.0218E-09	9.6717E-01
3.9000E-10	2.1090E+01	8.2251E-09	9.6713E-01
4.0000E-10	2.1060E+01	8.4240E-09	9.6709E-01
4.1000E-10	2.1040E+01	8.6264E-09	9.6705E-01
4.2000E-10	2.1010E+01	8.8242E-09	9.6701E-01
4.3000E-10	2.0990E+01	9.0257E-09	9.6698E-01
4.4000E-10	2.0970E+01	9.2268E-09	9.6694E-01
4.5000E-10	2.0940E+01	9.4230E-09	9.6691E-01
4.6000E-10	2.0920E+01	9.6232E-09	9.6687E-01
4.7000E-10	2.0900E+01	9.8230E-09	9.6684E-01
4.8000E-10	2.0880E+01	1.0022E-08	9.6680E-01
4.9000E-10	2.0860E+01	1.0221E-08	9.6677E-01
5.0000E-10	2.0840E+01	1.0420E-08	9.6674E-01
5.1000E-10	2.0820E+01	1.0618E-08	9.6674E-01
5.2000E-10	2.0800E+01	1.0816E-08	9.6673E-01
5.3000E-10	2.0780E+01	1.1013E-08	9.6670E-01
5.4000E-10	2.0760E+01	1.1210E-08	9.6665E-01

u	W(u)	uW(u)	Z(u)
5.5000E-10	2.0740E+01	1.1407E-08	9.6659E-01
5.6000E-10	2.0730E+01	1.1609E-08	9.6659E-01
5.7000E-10	2.0710E+01	1.1805E-08	9.6657E-01
5.8000E-10	2.0690E+01	1.2000E-08	9.6654E-01
5.9000E-10	2.0670E+01	1.2195E-08	9.6650E-01
6.0000E-10	2.0660E+01	1.2396E-08	9.6644E-01
6.1000E-10	2.0640E+01	1.2590E-08	9.6644E-01
6.2000E-10	2.0620E+01	1.2784E-08	9.6643E-01
6.3000E-10	2.0610E+01	1.2984E-08	9.6640E-01
6.4000E-10	2.0590E+01	1.3178E-08	9.6636E-01
6.5000E-10	2.0580E+01	1.3377E-08	9.6631E-01
6.6000E-10	2.0560E+01	1.3570E-08	9.6631E-01
6.7000E-10	2.0550E+01	1.3769E-08	9.6630E-01
6.8000E-10	2.0530E+01	1.3960E-08	9.6627E-01
6.9000E-10	2.0520E+01	1.4159E-08	9.6624E-01
7.0000E-10	2.0500E+01	1.4350E-08	9.6619E-01
7.1000E-10	2.0490E+01	1.4548E-08	9.6619E-01
7.2000E-10	2.0470E+01	1.4738E-08	9.6617E-01
7.3000E-10	2.0460E+01	1.4936E-08	9.6615E-01
7.4000E-10	2.0450E+01	1.5133E-08	9.6612E-01
7.5000E-10	2.0430E+01	1.5323E-08	9.6608E-01
7.6000E-10	2.0420E+01	1.5519E-08	9.6607E-01
7.7000E-10	2.0410E+01	1.5716E-08	9.6606E-01
7.8000E-10	2.0390E+01	1.5904E-08	9.6604E-01
7.9000E-10	2.0380E+01	1.6100E-08	9.6601E-01
8.0000E-10	2.0370E+01	1.6296E-08	9.6597E-01
8.1000E-10	2.0360E+01	1.6492E-08	9.6596E-01
8.2000E-10	2.0340E+01	1.6679E-08	9.6595E-01
8.3000E-10	2.0330E+01	1.6874E-08	9.6593E-01
8.4000E-10	2.0320E+01	1.7069E-08	9.6590E-01
8.5000E-10	2.0310E+01	1.7264E-08	9.6587E-01
8.6000E-10	2.0300E+01	1.7458E-08	9.6586E-01
8.7000E-10	2.0290E+01	1.7652E-08	9.6585E-01
8.8000E-10	2.0270E+01	1.7838E-08	9.6583E-01
8.9000E-10	2.0260E+01	1.8031E-08	9.6580E-01
9.0000E-10	2.0250E+01	1.8225E-08	9.6577E-01
9.1000E-10	2.0240E+01	1.8418E-08	9.6577E-01
9.2000E-10	2.0230E+01	1.8612E-08	9.6575E-01
9.3000E-10	2.0220E+01	1.8805E-08	9.6573E-01
9.4000E-10	2.0210E+01	1.8997E-08	9.6571E-01
9.5000E-10	2.0200E+01	1.9190E-08	9.6568E-01
9.6000E-10	2.0190E+01	1.9382E-08	9.6567E-01
9.7000E-10	2.0180E+01	1.9575E-08	9.6566E-01
9.8000E-10	2.0170E+01	1.9767E-08	9.6564E-01
9.9000E-10	2.0160E+01	1.9958E-08	9.6562E-01
1.0000E-09	2.0150E+01	2.0150E-08	9.6559E-01
1.1000E-09	2.0050E+01	2.2055E-08	9.6543E-01
1.2000E-09	1.9960E+01	2.3952E-08	9.6528E-01
1.3000E-09	1.9880E+01	2.5844E-08	9.6514E-01
1.4000E-09	1.9810E+01	2.7734E-08	9.6501E-01

u	W(u)	uW(u)	Z(u)
1.5000E-09	1.9740E+01	2.9610E-08	9.6489E-01
1.6000E-09	1.9680E+01	3.1488E-08	9.6477E-01
1.7000E-09	1.9620E+01	3.3354E-08	9.6466E-01
1.8000E-09	1.9560E+01	3.5208E-08	9.6456E-01
1.9000E-09	1.9500E+01	3.7050E-08	9.6446E-01
2.0000E-09	1.9450E+01	3.8900E-08	9.6437E-01
2.1000E-09	1.9400E+01	4.0740E-08	9.6428E-01
2.2000E-09	1.9360E+01	4.2592E-08	9.6419E-01
2.3000E-09	1.9310E+01	4.4413E-08	9.6411E-01
2.4000E-09	1.9270E+01	4.6248E-08	9.6403E-01
2.5000E-09	1.9230E+01	4.8075E-08	9.6395E-01
2.6000E-09	1.9190E+01	4.9894E-08	9.6388E-01
2.7000E-09	1.9150E+01	5.1705E-08	9.6381E-01
2.8000E-09	1.9120E+01	5.3536E-08	9.6374E-01
2.9000E-09	1.9080E+01	5.5332E-08	9.6367E-01
3.0000E-09	1.9050E+01	5.7150E-08	9.6361E-01
3.1000E-09	1.9010E+01	5.8931E-08	9.6355E-01
3.2000E-09	1.8980E+01	6.0736E-08	9.6349E-01
3.3000E-09	1.8950E+01	6.2535E-08	9.6343E-01
3.4000E-09	1.8920E+01	6.4328E-08	9.6337E-01
3.5000E-09	1.8890E+01	6.6115E-08	9.6331E-01
3.6000E-09	1.8870E+01	6.7932E-08	9.6326E-01
3.7000E-09	1.8840E+01	6.9708E-08	9.6320E-01
3.8000E-09	1.8810E+01	7.1478E-08	9.6315E-01
3.9000E-09	1.8790E+01	7.3281E-08	9.6310E-01
4.0000E-09	1.8760E+01	7.5040E-08	9.6305E-01
4.1000E-09	1.8740E+01	7.6834E-08	9.6300E-01
4.2000E-09	1.8710E+01	7.8582E-08	9.6296E-01
4.3000E-09	1.8690E+01	8.0367E-08	9.6291E-01
4.4000E-09	1.8660E+01	8.2104E-08	9.6286E-01
4.5000E-09	1.8640E+01	8.3880E-08	9.6282E-01
4.6000E-09	1.8620E+01	8.5652E-08	9.6277E-01
4.7000E-09	1.8600E+01	8.7420E-08	9.6273E-01
4.8000E-09	1.8580E+01	8.9184E-08	9.6269E-01
4.9000E-09	1.8560E+01	9.0944E-08	9.6265E-01
5.0000E-09	1.8540E+01	9.2700E-08	9.6261E-01
5.1000E-09	1.8520E+01	9.4452E-08	9.6261E-01
5.2000E-09	1.8500E+01	9.6200E-08	9.6259E-01
5.3000E-09	1.8480E+01	9.7944E-08	9.6255E-01
5.4000E-09	1.8460E+01	9.9684E-08	9.6249E-01
5.5000E-09	1.8440E+01	1.0142E-07	9.6241E-01
5.6000E-09	1.8420E+01	1.0315E-07	9.6241E-01
5.7000E-09	1.8410E+01	1.0494E-07	9.6239E-01
5.8000E-09	1.8390E+01	1.0666E-07	9.6235E-01
5.9000E-09	1.8370E+01	1.0838E-07	9.6230E-01
6.0000E-09	1.8350E+01	1.1010E-07	9.6224E-01
6.1000E-09	1.8340E+01	1.1187E-07	9.6223E-01
6.2000E-09	1.8320E+01	1.1358E-07	9.6221E-01
6.3000E-09	1.8310E+01	1.1535E-07	9.6218E-01
6.4000E-09	1.8290E+01	1.1706E-07	9.6213E-01

u	W(u)	uW(u)	Z(u)
6.5000E-09	1.8270E+01	1.1876E-07	9.6207E-01
6.6000E-09	1.8260E+01	1.2052E-07	9.6206E-01
6.7000E-09	1.8240E+01	1.2221E-07	9.6204E-01
6.8000E-09	1.8230E+01	1.2396E-07	9.6201E-01
6.9000E-09	1.8210E+01	1.2565E-07	9.6197E-01
7.0000E-09	1.8200E+01	1.2740E-07	9.6192E-01
7.1000E-09	1.8190E+01	1.2915E-07	9.6191E-01
7.2000E-09	1.8170E+01	1.3082E-07	9.6189E-01
7.3000E-09	1.8160E+01	1.3257E-07	9.6186E-01
7.4000E-09	1.8140E+01	1.3424E-07	9.6182E-01
7.5000E-09	1.8130E+01	1.3597E-07	9.6177E-01
7.6000E-09	1.8120E+01	1.3771E-07	9.6176E-01
7.7000E-09	1.8100E+01	1.3937E-07	9.6174E-01
7.8000E-09	1.8090E+01	1.4110E-07	9.6172E-01
7.9000E-09	1.8080E+01	1.4283E-07	9.6168E-01
8.0000E-09	1.8070E+01	1.4456E-07	9.6163E-01
8.1000E-09	1.8050E+01	1.4621E-07	9.6162E-01
8.2000E-09	1.8040E+01	1.4793E-07	9.6161E-01
8.3000E-09	1.8030E+01	1.4965E-07	9.6158E-01
8.4000E-09	1.8020E+01	1.5137E-07	9.6155E-01
8.5000E-09	1.8010E+01	1.5309E-07	9.6150E-01
8.6000E-09	1.7990E+01	1.5471E-07	9.6149E-01
8.7000E-09	1.7980E+01	1.5643E-07	9.6148E-01
8.8000E-09	1.7970E+01	1.5814E-07	9.6145E-01
8.9000E-09	1.7960E+01	1.5984E-07	9.6142E-01
9.0000E-09	1.7950E+01	1.6155E-07	9.6138E-01
9.1000E-09	1.7940E+01	1.6325E-07	9.6137E-01
9.2000E-09	1.7930E+01	1.6496E-07	9.6135E-01
9.3000E-09	1.7920E+01	1.6666E-07	9.6133E-01
9.4000E-09	1.7910E+01	1.6835E-07	9.6130E-01
9.5000E-09	1.7890E+01	1.6996E-07	9.6127E-01
9.6000E-09	1.7880E+01	1.7165E-07	9.6125E-01
9.7000E-09	1.7870E+01	1.7334E-07	9.6124E-01
9.8000E-09	1.7860E+01	1.7503E-07	9.6122E-01
9.9000E-09	1.7850E+01	1.7672E-07	9.6119E-01
1.0000E-08	1.7840E+01	1.7840E-07	9.6115E-01
1.1000E-08	1.7750E+01	1.9525E-07	9.6095E-01
1.2000E-08	1.7660E+01	2.1192E-07	9.6075E-01
1.3000E-08	1.7580E+01	2.2854E-07	9.6057E-01
1.4000E-08	1.7510E+01	2.4514E-07	9.6041E-01
1.5000E-08	1.7440E+01	2.6160E-07	9.6025E-01
1.6000E-08	1.7370E+01	2.7792E-07	9.6010E-01
1.7000E-08	1.7310E+01	2.9427E-07	9.5996E-01
1.8000E-08	1.7260E+01	3.1068E-07	9.5983E-01
1.9000E-08	1.7200E+01	3.2680E-07	9.5970E-01
2.0000E-08	1.7150E+01	3.4300E-07	9.5958E-01
2.1000E-08	1.7100E+01	3.5910E-07	9.5947E-01
2.2000E-08	1.7060E+01	3.7532E-07	9.5936E-01
2.3000E-08	1.7010E+01	3.9123E-07	9.5925E-01
2.4000E-08	1.6970E+01	4.0728E-07	9.5915E-01

u	W(u)	uW(u)	Z(u)
2.5000E-08	1.6930E+01	4.2325E-07	9.5905E-01
2.6000E-08	1.6890E+01	4.3914E-07	9.5896E-01
2.7000E-08	1.6850E+01	4.5495E-07	9.5886E-01
2.8000E-08	1.6810E+01	4.7068E-07	9.5878E-01
2.9000E-08	1.6780E+01	4.8662E-07	9.5869E-01
3.0000E-08	1.6740E+01	5.0220E-07	9.5861E-01
3.1000E-08	1.6710E+01	5.1801E-07	9.5852E-01
3.2000E-08	1.6680E+01	5.3376E-07	9.5845E-01
3.3000E-08	1.6650E+01	5.4945E-07	9.5837E-01
3.4000E-08	1.6620E+01	5.6508E-07	9.5829E-01
3.5000E-08	1.6590E+01	5.8065E-07	9.5822E-01
3.6000E-08	1.6560E+01	5.9616E-07	9.5815E-01
3.7000E-08	1.6540E+01	6.1198E-07	9.5808E-01
3.8000E-08	1.6510E+01	6.2738E-07	9.5801E-01
3.9000E-08	1.6480E+01	6.4272E-07	9.5795E-01
4.0000E-08	1.6460E+01	6.5840E-07	9.5788E-01
4.1000E-08	1.6430E+01	6.7363E-07	9.5782E-01
4.2000E-08	1.6410E+01	6.8922E-07	9.5776E-01
4.3000E-08	1.6380E+01	7.0434E-07	9.5770E-01
4.4000E-08	1.6360E+01	7.1984E-07	9.5764E-01
4.5000E-08	1.6340E+01	7.3530E-07	9.5758E-01
4.6000E-08	1.6320E+01	7.5072E-07	9.5752E-01
4.7000E-08	1.6300E+01	7.6610E-07	9.5746E-01
4.8000E-08	1.6270E+01	7.8096E-07	9.5741E-01
4.9000E-08	1.6250E+01	7.9625E-07	9.5736E-01
5.0000E-08	1.6230E+01	8.1150E-07	9.5733E-01
5.1000E-08	1.6210E+01	8.2671E-07	9.5731E-01
5.2000E-08	1.6190E+01	8.4188E-07	9.5727E-01
5.3000E-08	1.6180E+01	8.5754E-07	9.5721E-01
5.4000E-08	1.6160E+01	8.7264E-07	9.5712E-01
5.5000E-08	1.6140E+01	8.8770E-07	9.5707E-01
5.6000E-08	1.6120E+01	9.0272E-07	9.5705E-01
5.7000E-08	1.6100E+01	9.1770E-07	9.5702E-01
5.8000E-08	1.6090E+01	9.3322E-07	9.5696E-01
5.9000E-08	1.6070E+01	9.4813E-07	9.5688E-01
6.0000E-08	1.6050E+01	9.6300E-07	9.5684E-01
6.1000E-08	1.6040E+01	9.7844E-07	9.5682E-01
6.2000E-08	1.6020E+01	9.9324E-07	9.5678E-01
6.3000E-08	1.6000E+01	1.0080E-06	9.5673E-01
6.4000E-08	1.5990E+01	1.0234E-06	9.5666E-01
6.5000E-08	1.5970E+01	1.0381E-06	9.5662E-01
6.6000E-08	1.5960E+01	1.0534E-06	9.5660E-01
6.7000E-08	1.5940E+01	1.0680E-06	9.5656E-01
6.8000E-08	1.5930E+01	1.0832E-06	9.5651E-01
6.9000E-08	1.5910E+01	1.0978E-06	9.5645E-01
7.0000E-08	1.5900E+01	1.1130E-06	9.5641E-01
7.1000E-08	1.5880E+01	1.1275E-06	9.5639E-01
7.2000E-08	1.5870E+01	1.1426E-06	9.5636E-01
7.3000E-08	1.5860E+01	1.1578E-06	9.5632E-01
7.4000E-08	1.5840E+01	1.1722E-06	9.5626E-01

u	W(u)	uW(u)	Z(u)
7.5000E-08	1.5830E+01	1.1873E-06	9.5622E-01
7.6000E-08	1.5820E+01	1.2023E-06	9.5620E-01
7.7000E-08	1.5800E+01	1.2166E-06	9.5617E-01
7.8000E-08	1.5790E+01	1.2316E-06	9.5613E-01
7.9000E-08	1.5780E+01	1.2466E-06	9.5608E-01
8.0000E-08	1.5760E+01	1.2608E-06	9.5604E-01
8.1000E-08	1.5750E+01	1.2758E-06	9.5602E-01
8.2000E-08	1.5740E+01	1.2907E-06	9.5599E-01
8.3000E-08	1.5730E+01	1.3056E-06	9.5595E-01
8.4000E-08	1.5720E+01	1.3205E-06	9.5590E-01
8.5000E-08	1.5700E+01	1.3345E-06	9.5587E-01
8.6000E-08	1.5690E+01	1.3493E-06	9.5585E-01
8.7000E-08	1.5680E+01	1.3642E-06	9.5582E-01
8.8000E-08	1.5670E+01	1.3790E-06	9.5578E-01
8.9000E-08	1.5660E+01	1.3937E-06	9.5574E-01
9.0000E-08	1.5650E+01	1.4085E-06	9.5571E-01
9.1000E-08	1.5640E+01	1.4232E-06	9.5569E-01
9.2000E-08	1.5620E+01	1.4370E-06	9.5566E-01
9.3000E-08	1.5610E+01	1.4517E-06	9.5563E-01
9.4000E-08	1.5600E+01	1.4664E-06	9.5558E-01
9.5000E-08	1.5590E+01	1.4811E-06	9.5555E-01
9.6000E-08	1.5580E+01	1.4957E-06	9.5553E-01
9.7000E-08	1.5570E+01	1.5103E-06	9.5551E-01
9.8000E-08	1.5560E+01	1.5249E-06	9.5547E-01
9.9000E-08	1.5550E+01	1.5395E-06	9.5543E-01
1.0000E-07	1.5540E+01	1.5540E-06	9.5530E-01
1.1000E-07	1.5450E+01	1.6995E-06	9.5516E-01
1.2000E-07	1.5360E+01	1.8432E-06	9.5490E-01
1.3000E-07	1.5280E+01	1.9864E-06	9.5466E-01
1.4000E-07	1.5200E+01	2.1280E-06	9.5444E-01
1.5000E-07	1.5140E+01	2.2710E-06	9.5423E-01
1.6000E-07	1.5070E+01	2.4112E-06	9.5403E-01
1.7000E-07	1.5010E+01	2.5517E-06	9.5384E-01
1.8000E-07	1.4950E+01	2.6910E-06	9.5366E-01
1.9000E-07	1.4900E+01	2.8310E-06	9.5350E-01
2.0000E-07	1.4850E+01	2.9700E-06	9.5333E-01
2.1000E-07	1.4800E+01	3.1080E-06	9.5318E-01
2.2000E-07	1.4750E+01	3.2450E-06	9.5303E-01
2.3000E-07	1.4710E+01	3.3833E-06	9.5289E-01
2.4000E-07	1.4670E+01	3.5208E-06	9.5275E-01
2.5000E-07	1.4620E+01	3.6550E-06	9.5262E-01
2.6000E-07	1.4590E+01	3.7934E-06	9.5249E-01
2.7000E-07	1.4550E+01	3.9285E-06	9.5237E-01
2.8000E-07	1.4510E+01	4.0628E-06	9.5225E-01
2.9000E-07	1.4480E+01	4.1992E-06	9.5213E-01
3.0000E-07	1.4440E+01	4.3320E-06	9.5202E-01
3.1000E-07	1.4410E+01	4.4671E-06	9.5191E-01
3.2000E-07	1.4380E+01	4.6016E-06	9.5180E-01
3.3000E-07	1.4350E+01	4.7355E-06	9.5170E-01
3.4000E-07	1.4320E+01	4.8688E-06	9.5160E-01

u	W(u)	uW(u)	Z(u)
3.5000E-07	1.4290E+01	5.0015E-06	9.5150E-01
3.6000E-07	1.4260E+01	5.1336E-06	9.5140E-01
3.7000E-07	1.4230E+01	5.2651E-06	9.5131E-01
3.8000E-07	1.4210E+01	5.3998E-06	9.5122E-01
3.9000E-07	1.4180E+01	5.5302E-06	9.5133E-01
4.0000E-07	1.4150E+01	5.6600E-06	9.5104E-01
4.1000E-07	1.4130E+01	5.7933E-06	9.5095E-01
4.2000E-07	1.4110E+01	5.9262E-06	9.5087E-01
4.3000E-07	1.4080E+01	6.0544E-06	9.5079E-01
4.4000E-07	1.4060E+01	6.1864E-06	9.5071E-01
4.5000E-07	1.4040E+01	6.3180E-06	9.5063E-01
4.6000E-07	1.4010E+01	6.4446E-06	9.5055E-01
4.7000E-07	1.3990E+01	6.5753E-06	9.5047E-01
4.8000E-07	1.3970E+01	6.7056E-06	9.5040E-01
4.9000E-07	1.3950E+01	6.8355E-06	9.5033E-01
5.0000E-07	1.3930E+01	6.9650E-06	9.5025E-01
5.1000E-07	1.3910E+01	7.0941E-06	9.5023E-01
5.2000E-07	1.3890E+01	7.2228E-06	9.5019E-01
5.3000E-07	1.3870E+01	7.3511E-06	9.5012E-01
5.4000E-07	1.3850E+01	7.4790E-06	9.5003E-01
5.5000E-07	1.3840E+01	7.6120E-06	9.4991E-01
5.6000E-07	1.3820E+01	7.7392E-06	9.4989E-01
5.7000E-07	1.3800E+01	7.8660E-06	9.4985E-01
5.8000E-07	1.3780E+01	7.9924E-06	9.4978E-01
5.9000E-07	1.3770E+01	8.1243E-06	9.4970E-01
6.0000E-07	1.3750E+01	8.2500E-06	9.4959E-01
6.1000E-07	1.3730E+01	8.3753E-06	9.4957E-01
6.2000E-07	1.3720E+01	8.5064E-06	9.4953E-01
6.3000E-07	1.3700E+01	8.6310E-06	9.4947E-01
6.4000E-07	1.3680E+01	8.7552E-06	9.4939E-01
6.5000E-07	1.3670E+01	8.8855E-06	9.4930E-01
6.6000E-07	1.3650E+01	9.0090E-06	9.4927E-01
6.7000E-07	1.3640E+01	9.1388E-06	9.4923E-01
6.8000E-07	1.3620E+01	9.2616E-06	9.4918E-01
6.9000E-07	1.3610E+01	9.3909E-06	9.4911E-01
7.0000E-07	1.3590E+01	9.5130E-06	9.4902E-01
7.1000E-07	1.3580E+01	9.6418E-06	9.4899E-01
7.2000E-07	1.3570E+01	9.7704E-06	9.4896E-01
7.3000E-07	1.3550E+01	9.8915E-06	9.4890E-01
7.4000E-07	1.3540E+01	1.0020E-05	9.4884E-01
7.5000E-07	1.3530E+01	1.0148E-05	9.4876E-01
7.6000E-07	1.3510E+01	1.0268E-05	9.4873E-01
7.7000E-07	1.3500E+01	1.0395E-05	9.4870E-01
7.8000E-07	1.3490E+01	1.0522E-05	9.4865E-01
7.9000E-07	1.3470E+01	1.0641E-05	9.4859E-01
8.0000E-07	1.3460E+01	1.0768E-05	9.4852E-01
8.1000E-07	1.3450E+01	1.0895E-05	9.4849E-01
8.2000E-07	1.3440E+01	1.1021E-05	9.4845E-01
8.3000E-07	1.3420E+01	1.1139E-05	9.4841E-01
8.4000E-07	1.3410E+01	1.1264E-05	9.4835E-01

u	W(u)	uW(u)	Z(u)
8.5000E-07	1.3400E+01	1.1390E-05	9.4828E-01
8.6000E-07	1.3390E+01	1.1515E-05	9.4825E-01
8.7000E-07	1.3380E+01	1.1641E-05	9.4822E-01
8.8000E-07	1.3370E+01	1.1766E-05	9.4818E-01
8.9000E-07	1.3350E+01	1.1882E-05	9.4812E-01
9.0000E-07	1.3340E+01	1.2006E-05	9.4806E-01
9.1000E-07	1.3330E+01	1.2130E-05	9.4803E-01
9.2000E-07	1.3320E+01	1.2254E-05	9.4800E-01
9.3000E-07	1.3310E+01	1.2378E-05	9.4796E-01
9.4000E-07	1.3300E+01	1.2502E-05	9.4791E-01
9.5000E-07	1.3290E+01	1.2626E-05	9.4785E-01
9.6000E-07	1.3280E+01	1.2749E-05	9.4782E-01
9.7000E-07	1.3270E+01	1.2872E-05	9.4779E-01
9.8000E-07	1.3260E+01	1.2995E-05	9.4775E-01
9.9000E-07	1.3250E+01	1.3118E-05	9.4770E-01
1.0000E-06	1.3240E+01	1.3240E-05	9.4765E-01
1.1000E-06	1.3140E+01	1.4454E-05	9.4727E-01
1.2000E-06	1.3060E+01	1.5672E-05	9.4691E-01
1.3000E-06	1.2980E+01	1.6874E-05	9.4659E-01
1.4000E-06	1.2900E+01	1.8060E-05	9.4628E-01
1.5000E-06	1.2830E+01	1.9245E-05	9.4599E-01
1.6000E-06	1.2770E+01	2.0432E-05	9.4572E-01
1.7000E-06	1.2710E+01	2.1607E-05	9.4546E-01
1.8000E-06	1.2650E+01	2.2770E-05	9.4521E-01
1.9000E-06	1.2600E+01	2.3940E-05	9.4498E-01
2.0000E-06	1.2550E+01	2.5100E-05	9.4475E-01
2.1000E-06	1.2500E+01	2.6250E-05	9.4453E-01
2.2000E-06	1.2450E+01	2.7390E-05	9.4433E-01
2.3000E-06	1.2410E+01	2.8543E-05	9.4413E-01
2.4000E-06	1.2360E+01	2.9664E-05	9.4394E-01
2.5000E-06	1.2320E+01	3.0800E-05	9.4375E-01
2.6000E-06	1.2280E+01	3.1928E-05	9.4357E-01
2.7000E-06	1.2250E+01	3.3075E-05	9.4340E-01
2.8000E-06	1.2210E+01	3.4188E-05	9.4323E-01
2.9000E-06	1.2170E+01	3.5293E-05	9.4306E-01
3.0000E-06	1.2140E+01	3.6420E-05	9.4290E-01
3.1000E-06	1.2110E+01	3.7541E-05	9.4275E-01
3.2000E-06	1.2080E+01	3.8656E-05	9.4260E-01
3.3000E-06	1.2040E+01	3.9732E-05	9.4245E-01
3.4000E-06	1.2010E+01	4.0834E-05	9.4231E-01
3.5000E-06	1.1990E+01	4.1965E-05	9.4217E-01
3.6000E-06	1.1960E+01	4.3056E-05	9.4203E-01
3.7000E-06	1.1930E+01	4.4141E-05	9.4190E-01
3.8000E-06	1.1900E+01	4.5220E-05	9.4177E-01
3.9000E-06	1.1880E+01	4.6332E-05	9.4164E-01
4.0000E-06	1.1850E+01	4.7400E-05	9.4152E-01
4.1000E-06	1.1830E+01	4.8503E-05	9.4140E-01
4.2000E-06	1.1800E+01	4.9560E-05	9.4128E-01
4.3000E-06	1.1780E+01	5.0654E-05	9.4116E-01
4.4000E-06	1.1760E+01	5.1744E-05	9.4104E-01

u	W(u)	uW(u)	Z(u)
4.5000E-06	1.1730E+01	5.2785E-05	9.4093E-01
4.6000E-06	1.1710E+01	5.3866E-05	9.4082E-01
4.7000E-06	1.1690E+01	5.4943E-05	9.4071E-01
4.8000E-06	1.1670E+01	5.6016E-05	9.4060E-01
4.9000E-06	1.1650E+01	5.7085E-05	9.4050E-01
5.0000E-06	1.1630E+01	5.8150E-05	9.4040E-01
5.1000E-06	1.1610E+01	5.9211E-05	9.4036E-01
5.2000E-06	1.1590E+01	6.0268E-05	9.4029E-01
5.3000E-06	1.1570E+01	6.1321E-05	9.4019E-01
5.4000E-06	1.1550E+01	6.2370E-05	9.4006E-01
5.5000E-06	1.1530E+01	6.3415E-05	9.3990E-01
5.6000E-06	1.1520E+01	6.4512E-05	9.3986E-01
5.7000E-06	1.1500E+01	6.5550E-05	9.3980E-01
5.8000E-06	1.1480E+01	6.6584E-05	9.3970E-01
5.9000E-06	1.1460E+01	6.7614E-05	9.3959E-01
6.0000E-06	1.1450E+01	6.8700E-05	9.3945E-01
6.1000E-06	1.1430E+01	6.9723E-05	9.3940E-01
6.2000E-06	1.1410E+01	7.0742E-05	9.3934E-01
6.3000E-06	1.1400E+01	7.1820E-05	9.3925E-01
6.4000E-06	1.1380E+01	7.2832E-05	9.3915E-01
6.5000E-06	1.1370E+01	7.3905E-05	9.3902E-01
6.6000E-06	1.1350E+01	7.4910E-05	9.3898E-01
6.7000E-06	1.1340E+01	7.5978E-05	9.3892E-01
6.8000E-06	1.1320E+01	7.6976E-05	9.3883E-01
6.9000E-06	1.1310E+01	7.8039E-05	9.3874E-01
7.0000E-06	1.1290E+01	7.9030E-05	9.3862E-01
7.1000E-06	1.1280E+01	8.0088E-05	9.3858E-01
7.2000E-06	1.1260E+01	8.1072E-05	9.3852E-01
7.3000E-06	1.1250E+01	8.2125E-05	9.3844E-01
7.4000E-06	1.1240E+01	8.3176E-05	9.3835E-01
7.5000E-06	1.1220E+01	8.4150E-05	9.3824E-01
7.6000E-06	1.1210E+01	8.5196E-05	9.3820E-01
7.7000E-06	1.1200E+01	8.6240E-05	9.3814E-01
7.8000E-06	1.1180E+01	8.7204E-05	9.3807E-01
7.9000E-06	1.1170E+01	8.8243E-05	9.3798E-01
8.0000E-06	1.1160E+01	8.9280E-05	9.3789E-01
8.1000E-06	1.1150E+01	9.0315E-05	9.3784E-01
8.2000E-06	1.1130E+01	9.1266E-05	9.3779E-01
8.3000E-06	1.1120E+01	9.2296E-05	9.3772E-01
8.4000E-06	1.1110E+01	9.3324E-05	9.3764E-01
8.5000E-06	1.1100E+01	9.4350E-05	9.3755E-01
8.6000E-06	1.1090E+01	9.5374E-05	9.3750E-01
8.7000E-06	1.1070E+01	9.6309E-05	9.3745E-01
8.8000E-06	1.1060E+01	9.7328E-05	9.3739E-01
8.9000E-06	1.1050E+01	9.8345E-05	9.3731E-01
9.0000E-06	1.1040E+01	9.9360E-05	9.3722E-01
9.1000E-06	1.1030E+01	1.0037E-04	9.3718E-01
9.2000E-06	1.1020E+01	1.0138E-04	9.3713E-01
9.3000E-06	1.1010E+01	1.0239E-04	9.3707E-01
9.4000E-06	1.1000E+01	1.0340E-04	9.3700E-01

u	W(u)	uW(u)	Z(u)
9.5000E-06	1.0990E+01	1.0441E-04	9.3691E-01
9.6000E-06	1.0980E+01	1.0541E-04	9.3687E-01
9.7000E-06	1.0970E+01	1.0641E-04	9.3682E-01
9.8000E-06	1.0960E+01	1.0741E-04	9.3676E-01
9.9000E-06	1.0950E+01	1.0841E-04	9.3670E-01
1.0000E-05	1.0940E+01	1.0940E-04	9.3662E-01
1.1000E-05	1.0840E+01	1.1924E-04	9.3606E-01
1.2000E-05	1.0750E+01	1.2900E-04	9.3554E-01
1.3000E-05	1.0670E+01	1.3871E-04	9.3506E-01
1.4000E-05	1.0600E+01	1.4840E-04	9.3461E-01
1.5000E-05	1.0530E+01	1.5795E-04	9.3418E-01
1.6000E-05	1.0470E+01	1.6752E-04	9.3377E-01
1.7000E-05	1.0410E+01	1.7697E-04	9.3339E-01
1.8000E-05	1.0350E+01	1.8630E-04	9.3302E-01
1.9000E-05	1.0290E+01	1.9551E-04	9.3267E-01
2.0000E-05	1.0240E+01	2.0480E-04	9.3233E-01
2.1000E-05	1.0190E+01	2.1399E-04	9.3201E-01
2.2000E-05	1.0150E+01	2.2330E-04	9.3169E-01
2.3000E-05	1.0100E+01	2.3230E-04	9.3139E-01
2.4000E-05	1.0060E+01	2.4144E-04	9.3110E-01
2.5000E-05	1.0020E+01	2.5050E-04	9.3082E-01
2.6000E-05	9.9800E+00	2.5948E-04	9.3055E-01
2.7000E-05	9.9400E+00	2.6838E-04	9.3029E-01
2.8000E-05	9.9100E+00	2.7748E-04	9.3003E-01
2.9000E-05	9.8700E+00	2.8623E-04	9.2978E-01
3.0000E-05	9.8400E+00	2.9520E-04	9.2954E-01
3.1000E-05	9.8000E+00	3.0380E-04	9.2931E-01
3.2000E-05	9.7700E+00	3.1264E-04	9.2908E-01
3.3000E-05	9.7400E+00	3.2142E-04	9.2885E-01
3.4000E-05	9.7100E+00	3.3014E-04	9.2863E-01
3.5000E-05	9.6800E+00	3.3880E-04	9.2842E-01
3.6000E-05	9.6500E+00	3.4740E-04	9.2821E-01
3.7000E-05	9.6300E+00	3.5631E-04	9.2801E-01
3.8000E-05	9.6000E+00	3.6480E-04	9.2781E-01
3.9000E-05	9.5700E+00	3.7323E-04	9.2761E-01
4.0000E-05	9.5500E+00	3.8200E-04	9.2742E-01
4.1000E-05	9.5200E+00	3.9032E-04	9.2723E-01
4.2000E-05	9.5000E+00	3.9900E-04	9.2705E-01
4.3000E-05	9.4800E+00	4.0764E-04	9.2687E-01
4.4000E-05	9.4500E+00	4.1580E-04	9.2669E-01
4.5000E-05	9.4300E+00	4.2435E-04	9.2651E-01
4.6000E-05	9.4100E+00	4.3286E-04	9.2634E-01
4.7000E-05	9.3900E+00	4.4133E-04	9.2617E-01
4.8000E-05	9.3700E+00	4.4976E-04	9.2601E-01
4.9000E-05	9.3500E+00	4.5815E-04	9.2584E-01
5.0000E-05	9.3300E+00	4.6650E-04	9.2568E-01
5.1000E-05	9.3100E+00	4.7481E-04	9.2561E-01
5.2000E-05	9.2900E+00	4.8308E-04	9.2549E-01
5.3000E-05	9.2700E+00	4.9131E-04	9.2533E-01
5.4000E-05	9.2500E+00	4.9950E-04	9.2514E-01

u	W(u)	uW(u)	Z(u)
5.5000E-05	9.2300E+00	5.0765E-04	9.2492E-01
5.6000E-05	9.2100E+00	5.1576E-04	9.2484E-01
5.7000E-05	9.2000E+00	5.2440E-04	9.2473E-01
5.8000E-05	9.1800E+00	5.3244E-04	9.2458E-01
5.9000E-05	9.1600E+00	5.4044E-04	9.2441E-01
6.0000E-05	9.1400E+00	5.4840E-04	9.2420E-01
6.1000E-05	9.1300E+00	5.5693E-04	9.2412E-01
6.2000E-05	9.1100E+00	5.6482E-04	9.2402E-01
6.3000E-05	9.1000E+00	5.7330E-04	9.2388E-01
6.4000E-05	9.0800E+00	5.8112E-04	9.2372E-01
6.5000E-05	9.0600E+00	5.8890E-04	9.2353E-01
6.6000E-05	9.0500E+00	5.9730E-04	9.2346E-01
6.7000E-05	9.0300E+00	6.0501E-04	9.2335E-01
6.8000E-05	9.0200E+00	6.1336E-04	9.2323E-01
6.9000E-05	9.0000E+00	6.2100E-04	9.2308E-01
7.0000E-05	8.9900E+00	6.2930E-04	9.2290E-01
7.1000E-05	8.9800E+00	6.3758E-04	9.2283E-01
7.2000E-05	8.9600E+00	6.4512E-04	9.2273E-01
7.3000E-05	8.9500E+00	6.5335E-04	9.2261E-01
7.4000E-05	8.9300E+00	6.6082E-04	9.2247E-01
7.5000E-05	8.9200E+00	6.6900E-04	9.2231E-01
7.6000E-05	8.9100E+00	6.7716E-04	9.2223E-01
7.7000E-05	8.8900E+00	6.8453E-04	9.2214E-01
7.8000E-05	8.8800E+00	6.9264E-04	9.2202E-01
7.9000E-05	8.8700E+00	7.0073E-04	9.2189E-01
8.0000E-05	8.8600E+00	7.0880E-04	9.2174E-01
8.1000E-05	8.8400E+00	7.1604E-04	9.2167E-01
8.2000E-05	8.8300E+00	7.2406E-04	9.2158E-01
8.3000E-05	8.8200E+00	7.3206E-04	9.2147E-01
8.4000E-05	8.8100E+00	7.4004E-04	9.2134E-01
8.5000E-05	8.8000E+00	7.4800E-04	9.2120E-01
8.6000E-05	8.7800E+00	7.5508E-04	9.2113E-01
8.7000E-05	8.7700E+00	7.6299E-04	9.2104E-01
8.8000E-05	8.7600E+00	7.7088E-04	9.2094E-01
8.9000E-05	8.7500E+00	7.7875E-04	9.2082E-01
9.0000E-05	8.7400E+00	7.8660E-04	9.2069E-01
9.1000E-05	8.7300E+00	7.9443E-04	9.2062E-01
9.2000E-05	8.7200E+00	8.0224E-04	9.2053E-01
9.3000E-05	8.7100E+00	8.1003E-04	9.2043E-01
9.4000E-05	8.7000E+00	8.1780E-04	9.2032E-01
9.5000E-05	8.6800E+00	8.2460E-04	9.2020E-01
9.6000E-05	8.6700E+00	8.3232E-04	9.2013E-01
9.7000E-05	8.6600E+00	8.4002E-04	9.2004E-01
9.8000E-05	8.6500E+00	8.4770E-04	9.1995E-01
9.9000E-05	8.6400E+00	8.5536E-04	9.1984E-01
1.0000E-04	8.6300E+00	8.6300E-04	9.1972E-01
1.1000E-04	8.5400E+00	9.3940E-04	9.1883E-01
1.2000E-04	8.4500E+00	1.0140E-03	9.1799E-01
1.3000E-04	8.3700E+00	1.0881E-03	9.1721E-01
1.4000E-04	8.3000E+00	1.1620E-03	9.1647E-01

u	W(u)	uW(u)	Z(u)
1.5000E-04	8.2300E+00	1.2345E-03	9.1577E-01
1.6000E-04	8.1600E+00	1.3056E-03	9.1511E-01
1.7000E-04	8.1000E+00	1.3770E-03	9.1448E-01
1.8000E-04	8.0500E+00	1.4490E-03	9.1387E-01
1.9000E-04	7.9900E+00	1.5181E-03	9.1329E-01
2.0000E-04	7.9400E+00	1.5880E-03	9.1273E-01
2.1000E-04	7.8900E+00	1.6569E-03	9.1219E-01
2.2000E-04	7.8400E+00	1.7248E-03	9.1167E-01
2.3000E-04	7.8000E+00	1.7940E-03	9.1117E-01
2.4000E-04	7.7600E+00	1.8624E-03	9.1068E-01
2.5000E-04	7.7200E+00	1.9300E-03	9.1021E-01
2.6000E-04	7.6800E+00	1.9968E-03	9.0976E-01
2.7000E-04	7.6400E+00	2.0628E-03	9.0931E-01
2.8000E-04	7.6000E+00	2.1280E-03	9.0888E-01
2.9000E-04	7.5700E+00	2.1953E-03	9.0846E-01
3.0000E-04	7.5300E+00	2.2590E-03	9.0805E-01
3.1000E-04	7.5000E+00	2.3250E-03	9.0765E-01
3.2000E-04	7.4700E+00	2.3904E-03	9.0726E-01
3.3000E-04	7.4400E+00	2.4552E-03	9.0687E-01
3.4000E-04	7.4100E+00	2.5194E-03	9.0650E-01
3.5000E-04	7.3800E+00	2.5830E-03	9.0613E-01
3.6000E-04	7.3500E+00	2.6460E-03	9.0578E-01
3.7000E-04	7.3300E+00	2.7121E-03	9.0543E-01
3.8000E-04	7.3000E+00	2.7740E-03	9.0508E-01
3.9000E-04	7.2700E+00	2.8353E-03	9.0474E-01
4.0000E-04	7.2500E+00	2.9000E-03	9.0441E-01
4.1000E-04	7.2200E+00	2.9602E-03	9.0409E-01
4.2000E-04	7.2000E+00	3.0240E-03	9.0377E-01
4.3000E-04	7.1700E+00	3.0831E-03	9.0345E-01
4.4000E-04	7.1500E+00	3.1460E-03	9.0314E-01
4.5000E-04	7.1300E+00	3.2085E-03	9.0284E-01
4.6000E-04	7.1100E+00	3.2706E-03	9.0254E-01
4.7000E-04	7.0900E+00	3.3323E-03	9.0225E-01
4.8000E-04	7.0600E+00	3.3888E-03	9.0196E-01
4.9000E-04	7.0400E+00	3.4496E-03	9.0167E-01
5.0000E-04	7.0200E+00	3.5100E-03	9.0139E-01
5.1000E-04	7.0000E+00	3.5700E-03	9.0122E-01
5.2000E-04	6.9800E+00	3.6296E-03	9.0100E-01
5.3000E-04	6.9700E+00	3.6941E-03	9.0073E-01
5.4000E-04	6.9500E+00	3.7530E-03	9.0041E-01
5.5000E-04	6.9300E+00	3.8115E-03	9.0004E-01
5.6000E-04	6.9100E+00	3.8696E-03	8.9987E-01
5.7000E-04	6.8900E+00	3.9273E-03	8.9966E-01
5.8000E-04	6.8800E+00	3.9904E-03	8.9941E-01
5.9000E-04	6.8600E+00	4.0474E-03	8.9911E-01
6.0000E-04	6.8400E+00	4.1040E-03	8.9878E-01
6.1000E-04	6.8300E+00	4.1663E-03	8.9861E-01
6.2000E-04	6.8100E+00	4.2222E-03	8.9841E-01
6.3000E-04	6.7900E+00	4.2777E-03	8.9817E-01
6.4000E-04	6.7800E+00	4.3392E-03	8.9790E-01

u	W(u)	uW(u)	Z(u)
6.5000E-04	6.7600E+00	4.3940E-03	8.9759E-01
6.6000E-04	6.7500E+00	4.4550E-03	8.9743E-01
6.7000E-04	6.7300E+00	4.5091E-03	8.9723E-01
6.8000E-04	6.7200E+00	4.5696E-03	8.9700E-01
6.9000E-04	6.7000E+00	4.6230E-03	8.9675E-01
7.0000E-04	6.6900E+00	4.6830E-03	8.9646E-01
7.1000E-04	6.6700E+00	4.7357E-03	8.9630E-01
7.2000E-04	6.6600E+00	4.7952E-03	8.9611E-01
7.3000E-04	6.6500E+00	4.8545E-03	8.9590E-01
7.4000E-04	6.6300E+00	4.9062E-03	8.9566E-01
7.5000E-04	6.6200E+00	4.9650E-03	8.9539E-01
7.6000E-04	6.6100E+00	5.0236E-03	8.9524E-01
7.7000E-04	6.5900E+00	5.0743E-03	8.9505E-01
7.8000E-04	6.5800E+00	5.1324E-03	8.9485E-01
7.9000E-04	6.5700E+00	5.1903E-03	8.9462E-01
8.0000E-04	6.5500E+00	5.2400E-03	8.9437E-01
8.1000E-04	6.5400E+00	5.2974E-03	8.9422E-01
8.2000E-04	6.5300E+00	5.3546E-03	8.9404E-01
8.3000E-04	6.5200E+00	5.4116E-03	8.9385E-01
8.4000E-04	6.5100E+00	5.4684E-03	8.9363E-01
8.5000E-04	6.4900E+00	5.5165E-03	8.9339E-01
8.6000E-04	6.4800E+00	5.5728E-03	8.9324E-01
8.7000E-04	6.4700E+00	5.6289E-03	8.9307E-01
8.8000E-04	6.4600E+00	5.6848E-03	8.9289E-01
8.9000E-04	6.4500E+00	5.7405E-03	8.9268E-01
9.0000E-04	6.4400E+00	5.7960E-03	8.9245E-01
9.1000E-04	6.4300E+00	5.8513E-03	8.9231E-01
9.2000E-04	6.4100E+00	5.8972E-03	8.9214E-01
9.3000E-04	6.4000E+00	5.9520E-03	8.9196E-01
9.4000E-04	6.3900E+00	6.0066E-03	8.9177E-01
9.5000E-04	6.3800E+00	6.0610E-03	8.9155E-01
9.6000E-04	6.3700E+00	6.1152E-03	8.9141E-01
9.7000E-04	6.3600E+00	6.1692E-03	8.9125E-01
9.8000E-04	6.3500E+00	6.2230E-03	8.9108E-01
9.9000E-04	6.3400E+00	6.2766E-03	8.9089E-01
1.0000E-03	6.3300E+00	6.3300E-03	8.9068E-01
1.1000E-03	6.2400E+00	6.8640E-03	8.8903E-01
1.2000E-03	6.1500E+00	7.3800E-03	8.8748E-01
1.3000E-03	6.0700E+00	7.8910E-03	8.8601E-01
1.4000E-03	6.0000E+00	8.4000E-03	8.8462E-01
1.5000E-03	5.9300E+00	8.8950E-03	8.8330E-01
1.6000E-03	5.8600E+00	9.3760E-03	8.8203E-01
1.7000E-03	5.8000E+00	9.8600E-03	8.8082E-01
1.8000E-03	5.7400E+00	1.0332E-02	8.7965E-01
1.9000E-03	5.6900E+00	1.0811E-02	8.7853E-01
2.0000E-03	5.6400E+00	1.1280E-02	8.7744E-01
2.1000E-03	5.5900E+00	1.1739E-02	8.7639E-01
2.2000E-03	5.5400E+00	1.2188E-02	8.7538E-01
2.3000E-03	5.5000E+00	1.2650E-02	8.7439E-01
2.4000E-03	5.4600E+00	1.3104E-02	8.7343E-01

u	W(u)	uW(u)	Z(u)
2.5000E-03	5.4200E+00	1.3550E-02	8.7250E-01
2.6000E-03	5.3800E+00	1.3988E-02	8.7159E-01
2.7000E-03	5.3400E+00	1.4418E-02	8.7070E-01
2.8000E-03	5.3000E+00	1.4840E-02	8.6984E-01
2.9000E-03	5.2700E+00	1.5283E-02	8.6899E-01
3.0000E-03	5.2300E+00	1.5690E-02	8.6816E-01
3.1000E-03	5.2000E+00	1.6120E-02	8.6735E-01
3.2000E-03	5.1700E+00	1.6544E-02	8.6656E-01
3.3000E-03	5.1400E+00	1.6962E-02	8.6579E-01
3.4000E-03	5.1100E+00	1.7374E-02	8.6502E-01
3.5000E-03	5.0800E+00	1.7780E-02	8.6428E-01
3.6000E-03	5.0500E+00	1.8180E-02	8.6354E-01
3.7000E-03	5.0300E+00	1.8611E-02	8.6282E-01
3.8000E-03	5.0000E+00	1.9000E-02	8.6211E-01
3.9000E-03	4.9700E+00	1.9383E-02	8.6141E-01
4.0000E-03	4.9500E+00	1.9800E-02	8.6073E-01
4.1000E-03	4.9200E+00	2.0172E-02	8.6005E-01
4.2000E-03	4.9000E+00	2.0580E-02	8.5939E-01
4.3000E-03	4.8800E+00	2.0984E-02	8.5873E-01
4.4000E-03	4.8500E+00	2.1340E-02	8.5809E-01
4.5000E-03	4.8300E+00	2.1735E-02	8.5745E-01
4.6000E-03	4.8100E+00	2.2126E-02	8.5682E-01
4.7000E-03	4.7900E+00	2.2513E-02	8.5620E-01
4.8000E-03	4.7700E+00	2.2896E-02	8.5559E-01
4.9000E-03	4.7500E+00	2.3275E-02	8.5499E-01
5.0000E-03	4.7300E+00	2.3650E-02	8.5439E-01
5.1000E-03	4.7100E+00	2.4021E-02	8.5396E-01
5.2000E-03	4.6900E+00	2.4388E-02	8.5345E-01
5.3000E-03	4.6700E+00	2.4751E-02	8.5288E-01
5.4000E-03	4.6500E+00	2.5110E-02	8.5223E-01
5.5000E-03	4.6300E+00	2.5465E-02	8.5152E-01
5.6000E-03	4.6100E+00	2.5816E-02	8.5110E-01
5.7000E-03	4.6000E+00	2.6220E-02	8.5061E-01
5.8000E-03	4.5800E+00	2.6564E-02	8.5007E-01
5.9000E-03	4.5600E+00	2.6904E-02	8.4946E-01
6.0000E-03	4.5400E+00	2.7240E-02	8.4880E-01
6.1000E-03	4.5300E+00	2.7633E-02	8.4839E-01
6.2000E-03	4.5100E+00	2.7962E-02	8.4792E-01
6.3000E-03	4.5000E+00	2.8350E-02	8.4740E-01
6.4000E-03	4.4800E+00	2.8672E-02	8.4684E-01
6.5000E-03	4.4700E+00	2.9055E-02	8.4622E-01
6.6000E-03	4.4500E+00	2.9370E-02	8.4522E-01
6.7000E-03	4.4400E+00	2.9748E-02	8.4537E-01
6.8000E-03	4.4200E+00	3.0056E-02	8.4487E-01
6.9000E-03	4.4100E+00	3.0429E-02	8.4433E-01
7.0000E-03	4.3900E+00	3.0730E-02	8.4375E-01
7.1000E-03	4.3800E+00	3.1098E-02	8.4336E-01
7.2000E-03	4.3600E+00	3.1392E-02	8.4293E-01
7.3000E-03	4.3500E+00	3.1755E-02	8.4245E-01
7.4000E-03	4.3400E+00	3.2116E-02	8.4194E-01

u	W(u)	uW(u)	Z(u)
7.5000E-03	4.3200E+00	3.2400E-02	8.4139E-01
7.6000E-03	4.3100E+00	3.2756E-02	8.4101E-01
7.7000E-03	4.3000E+00	3.3110E-02	8.4059E-01
7.8000E-03	4.2800E+00	3.3384E-02	8.4014E-01
7.9000E-03	4.2700E+00	3.3733E-02	8.3965E-01
8.0000E-03	4.2600E+00	3.4080E-02	8.3912E-01
8.1000E-03	4.2500E+00	3.4425E-02	8.3875E-01
8.2000E-03	4.2300E+00	3.4686E-02	8.3834E-01
8.3000E-03	4.2200E+00	3.5026E-02	8.3791E-01
8.4000E-03	4.2100E+00	3.5364E-02	8.3744E-01
8.5000E-03	4.2000E+00	3.5700E-02	8.3694E-01
8.6000E-03	4.1900E+00	3.6034E-02	8.3657E-01
8.7000E-03	4.1800E+00	3.6366E-02	8.3618E-01
8.8000E-03	4.1600E+00	3.6608E-02	8.3575E-01
8.9000E-03	4.1500E+00	3.6935E-02	8.3530E-01
9.0000E-03	4.1400E+00	3.7260E-02	8.3482E-01
9.1000E-03	4.1300E+00	3.7583E-02	8.3447E-01
9.2000E-03	4.1200E+00	3.7904E-02	8.3408E-01
9.3000E-03	4.1100E+00	3.8223E-02	8.3368E-01
9.4000E-03	4.1000E+00	3.8540E-02	8.3324E-01
9.5000E-03	4.0900E+00	3.8855E-02	8.3278E-01
9.6000E-03	4.0800E+00	3.9168E-02	8.3243E-01
9.7000E-03	4.0700E+00	3.9479E-02	8.3206E-01
9.8000E-03	4.0600E+00	3.9788E-02	8.3166E-01
9.9000E-03	4.0500E+00	4.0095E-02	8.3124E-01
1.0000E-02	4.0400E+00	4.0400E-02	8.3080E-01
1.1000E-02	3.9400E+00	4.3340E-02	8.2700E-01
1.2000E-02	3.8600E+00	4.6320E-02	8.2340E-01
1.3000E-02	3.7800E+00	4.9140E-02	8.1997E-01
1.4000E-02	3.7100E+00	5.1940E-02	8.1668E-01
1.5000E-02	3.6400E+00	5.4600E-02	8.1352E-01
1.6000E-02	3.5700E+00	5.7120E-02	8.1048E-01
1.7000E-02	3.5100E+00	5.9670E-02	8.0754E-01
1.8000E-02	3.4600E+00	6.2280E-02	8.0469E-01
1.9000E-02	3.4100E+00	6.4790E-02	8.0194E-01
2.0000E-02	3.3500E+00	6.7000E-02	7.9925E-01
2.1000E-02	3.3100E+00	6.9510E-02	7.9665E-01
2.2000E-02	3.2600E+00	7.1720E-02	7.9410E-01
2.3000E-02	3.2200E+00	7.4060E-02	7.9162E-01
2.4000E-02	3.1800E+00	7.6320E-02	7.8920E-01
2.5000E-02	3.1400E+00	7.8500E-02	7.8683E-01
2.6000E-02	3.1000E+00	8.0600E-02	7.8451E-01
2.7000E-02	3.0600E+00	8.2620E-02	7.8224E-01
2.8000E-02	3.0300E+00	8.4840E-02	7.8001E-01
2.9000E-02	2.9900E+00	8.6710E-02	7.7782E-01
3.0000E-02	2.9600E+00	8.8800E-02	7.7567E-01
3.1000E-02	2.9300E+00	9.0830E-02	7.7356E-01
3.2000E-02	2.9000E+00	9.2800E-02	7.7149E-01
3.3000E-02	2.8700E+00	9.4710E-02	7.6944E-01
3.4000E-02	2.8400E+00	9.6560E-02	7.6743E-01

u	W(u)	uW(u)	Z(u)
3.5000E-02	2.8100E+00	9.8350E-02	7.6545E-01
3.6000E-02	2.7800E+00	1.0008E-01	7.6350E-01
3.7000E-02	2.7600E+00	1.0212E-01	7.6158E-01
3.8000E-02	2.7300E+00	1.0374E-01	7.5968E-01
3.9000E-02	2.7100E+00	1.0569E-01	7.5781E-01
4.0000E-02	2.6800E+00	1.0720E-01	7.5597E-01
4.1000E-02	2.6600E+00	1.0906E-01	7.5414E-01
4.2000E-02	2.6300E+00	1.1046E-01	7.5234E-01
4.3000E-02	2.6100E+00	1.1223E-01	7.5056E-01
4.4000E-02	2.5900E+00	1.1396E-01	7.4880E-01
4.5000E-02	2.5700E+00	1.1565E-01	7.4707E-01
4.6000E-02	2.5500E+00	1.1730E-01	7.4535E-01
4.7000E-02	2.5300E+00	1.1891E-01	7.4365E-01
4.8000E-02	2.5100E+00	1.2048E-01	7.4197E-01
4.9000E-02	2.4900E+00	1.2201E-01	7.4030E-01
5.0000E-02	2.4700E+00	1.2350E-01	7.3866E-01
5.1000E-02	2.4500E+00	1.2495E-01	7.3733E-01
5.2000E-02	2.4300E+00	1.2636E-01	7.3586E-01
5.3000E-02	2.4100E+00	1.2773E-01	7.3426E-01
5.4000E-02	2.3900E+00	1.2906E-01	7.3252E-01
5.5000E-02	2.3800E+00	1.3090E-01	7.3066E-01
5.6000E-02	2.3600E+00	1.3216E-01	7.2936E-01
5.7000E-02	2.3400E+00	1.3338E-01	7.2795E-01
5.8000E-02	2.3300E+00	1.3514E-01	7.2642E-01
5.9000E-02	2.3100E+00	1.3629E-01	7.2477E-01
6.0000E-02	2.3000E+00	1.3800E-01	7.2302E-01
6.1000E-02	2.2800E+00	1.3908E-01	7.2175E-01
6.2000E-02	2.2600E+00	1.4012E-01	7.2039E-01
6.3000E-02	2.2500E+00	1.4175E-01	7.1892E-01
6.4000E-02	2.2300E+00	1.4272E-01	7.1735E-01
6.5000E-02	2.2200E+00	1.4430E-01	7.1569E-01
6.6000E-02	2.2100E+00	1.4586E-01	7.1445E-01
6.7000E-02	2.1900E+00	1.4673E-01	7.1313E-01
6.8000E-02	2.1800E+00	1.4824E-01	7.1172E-01
6.9000E-02	2.1600E+00	1.4904E-01	7.1022E-01
7.0000E-02	2.1500E+00	1.5050E-01	7.0863E-01
7.1000E-02	2.1400E+00	1.5194E-01	7.0743E-01
7.2000E-02	2.1200E+00	1.5264E-01	7.0615E-01
7.3000E-02	2.1100E+00	1.5403E-01	7.0478E-01
7.4000E-02	2.1000E+00	1.5540E-01	7.0334E-01
7.5000E-02	2.0900E+00	1.5675E-01	7.0182E-01
7.6000E-02	2.0700E+00	1.5732E-01	7.0065E-01
7.7000E-02	2.0600E+00	1.5862E-01	6.9940E-01
7.8000E-02	2.0500E+00	1.5990E-01	6.9808E-01
7.9000E-02	2.0400E+00	1.6116E-01	6.9669E-01
8.0000E-02	2.0300E+00	1.6240E-01	6.9523E-01
8.1000E-02	2.0200E+00	1.6362E-01	6.9408E-01
8.2000E-02	2.0000E+00	1.6400E-01	6.9287E-01
8.3000E-02	1.9930E+00	1.6542E-01	6.9159E-01
8.4000E-02	1.9820E+00	1.6649E-01	6.9025E-01

u	W(u)	uW(u)	Z(u)
8.5000E-02	1.9710E+00	1.6754E-01	6.8884E-01
8.6000E-02	1.9600E+00	1.6856E-01	6.8772E-01
8.7000E-02	1.9500E+00	1.6965E-01	6.8654E-01
8.8000E-02	1.9390E+00	1.7063E-01	6.8529E-01
8.9000E-02	1.9290E+00	1.7168E-01	6.8399E-01
9.0000E-02	1.9190E+00	1.7271E-01	6.8263E-01
9.1000E-02	1.9090E+00	1.7372E-01	6.8153E-01
9.2000E-02	1.8990E+00	1.7471E-01	6.8038E-01
9.3000E-02	1.8890E+00	1.7568E-01	6.7917E-01
9.4000E-02	1.8790E+00	1.7663E-01	6.7791E-01
9.5000E-02	1.8690E+00	1.7756E-01	6.7659E-01
9.6000E-02	1.8600E+00	1.7856E-01	6.7552E-01
9.7000E-02	1.8510E+00	1.7955E-01	6.7439E-01
9.8000E-02	1.8410E+00	1.8042E-01	6.7321E-01
9.9000E-02	1.8320E+00	1.8137E-01	6.7199E-01
1.0000E-01	1.8230E+00	1.8230E-01	6.7071E-01
1.1000E-01	1.7370E+00	1.9107E-01	6.5936E-01
1.2000E-01	1.6600E+00	1.9920E-01	6.4852E-01
1.3000E-01	1.5890E+00	2.0657E-01	6.3811E-01
1.4000E-01	1.5240E+00	2.1336E-01	6.2810E-01
1.5000E-01	1.4640E+00	2.1960E-01	6.1844E-01
1.6000E-01	1.4090E+00	2.2544E-01	6.0910E-01
1.7000E-01	1.3580E+00	2.3086E-01	6.0006E-01
1.8000E-01	1.3100E+00	2.3580E-01	5.9128E-01
1.9000E-01	1.2650E+00	2.4035E-01	5.8276E-01
2.0000E-01	1.2230E+00	2.4460E-01	5.7447E-01
2.1000E-01	1.1830E+00	2.4843E-01	5.6640E-01
2.2000E-01	1.1450E+00	2.5190E-01	5.5853E-01
2.3000E-01	1.1100E+00	2.5530E-01	5.5085E-01
2.4000E-01	1.0760E+00	2.5824E-01	5.4335E-01
2.5000E-01	1.0440E+00	2.6100E-01	5.3603E-01
2.6000E-01	1.0140E+00	2.6364E-01	5.2886E-01
2.7000E-01	9.8500E-01	2.6595E-01	5.2185E-01
2.8000E-01	9.5700E-01	2.6796E-01	5.1499E-01
2.9000E-01	9.3100E-01	2.6999E-01	5.0827E-01
3.0000E-01	9.0600E-01	2.7180E-01	5.0168E-01
3.1000E-01	8.8200E-01	2.7342E-01	4.9522E-01
3.2000E-01	8.5800E-01	2.7456E-01	4.8888E-01
3.3000E-01	8.3600E-01	2.7588E-01	4.8319E-01
3.4000E-01	8.1500E-01	2.7710E-01	4.7622E-01
3.5000E-01	7.9400E-01	2.7790E-01	4.7090E-01
3.6000E-01	7.7400E-01	2.7864E-01	4.6483E-01
3.7000E-01	7.5500E-01	2.7935E-01	4.5933E-01
3.8000E-01	7.3700E-01	2.8006E-01	4.5312E-01
3.9000E-01	7.1900E-01	2.8041E-01	4.4757E-01
4.0000E-01	7.0200E-01	2.8080E-01	4.4278E-01
4.1000E-01	6.8600E-01	2.8126E-01	4.3737E-01
4.2000E-01	6.7000E-01	2.8140E-01	4.3134E-01
4.3000E-01	6.5500E-01	*2.8165E-01	4.2620E-01
4.4000E-01	6.4000E-01	2.8160E-01	4.2049E-01

u	W(u)	uW(u)	Z(u)
4.5000E-01	6.2500E-01	2.8125E-01	4.1578E-01
4.6000E-01	6.1100E-01	2.8106E-01	4.1054E-01
4.7000E-01	5.9800E-01	2.8106E-01	4.0644E-01
4.8000E-01	5.8500E-01	2.8080E-01	4.0186E-01
4.9000E-01	5.7200E-01	2.8028E-01	3.9679E-01
5.0000E-01	5.6000E-01	2.8000E-01	3.9123E-01
5.1000E-01	5.4800E-01	2.7948E-01	3.8772E-01
5.2000E-01	5.3600E-01	2.7872E-01	3.8380E-01
5.3000E-01	5.2500E-01	2.7825E-01	3.7947E-01
5.4000E-01	5.1400E-01	2.7756E-01	3.7471E-01
5.5000E-01	5.0300E-01	2.7665E-01	3.6952E-01
5.6000E-01	4.9300E-01	2.7608E-01	3.6592E-01
5.7000E-01	4.8300E-01	2.7531E-01	3.6294E-01
5.8000E-01	4.7300E-01	2.7434E-01	3.5760E-01
5.9000E-01	4.6400E-01	2.7376E-01	3.5286E-01
6.0000E-01	4.5400E-01	2.7240E-01	3.4774E-01
6.1000E-01	4.4500E-01	2.7145E-01	3.4446E-01
6.2000E-01	4.3700E-01	2.7094E-01	3.4086E-01
6.3000E-01	4.2800E-01	2.6964E-01	3.3693E-01
6.4000E-01	4.2000E-01	2.6880E-01	3.3267E-01
6.5000E-01	4.1200E-01	2.6780E-01	3.2767E-01
6.6000E-01	4.0400E-01	2.6664E-01	3.2475E-01
6.7000E-01	3.9600E-01	2.6532E-01	3.2172E-01
6.8000E-01	3.8800E-01	2.6384E-01	3.1856E-01
6.9000E-01	3.8100E-01	2.6289E-01	3.1444E-01
7.0000E-01	3.7400E-01	2.6180E-01	3.1016E-01
7.1000E-01	3.6700E-01	2.6057E-01	3.0736E-01
7.2000E-01	3.6000E-01	2.5920E-01	3.0444E-01
7.3000E-01	3.5300E-01	2.5769E-01	3.0142E-01
7.4000E-01	3.4700E-01	2.5678E-01	2.9741E-01
7.5000E-01	3.4000E-01	2.5500E-01	2.9412E-01
7.6000E-01	3.3400E-01	2.5384E-01	2.9102E-01
7.7000E-01	3.2800E-01	2.5256E-01	2.8780E-01
7.8000E-01	3.2200E-01	2.5116E-01	2.8447E-01
7.9000E-01	3.1600E-01	2.4964E-01	2.8101E-01
8.0000E-01	3.1100E-01	2.4880E-01	2.7653E-01
8.1000E-01	3.0500E-01	2.4705E-01	2.7475E-01
8.2000E-01	3.0000E-01	2.4600E-01	2.7200E-01
8.3000E-01	2.9400E-01	2.4402E-01	2.7007E-01
8.4000E-01	2.8900E-01	2.4276E-01	2.6713E-01
8.5000E-01	2.8400E-01	2.4140E-01	2.6408E-01
8.6000E-01	2.7900E-01	2.3994E-01	2.6165E-01
8.7000E-01	2.7400E-01	2.3838E-01	2.5912E-01
8.8000E-01	2.6900E-01	2.3672E-01	2.5651E-01
8.9000E-01	2.6500E-01	2.3585E-01	2.5283E-01
9.0000E-01	2.6000E-01	2.3400E-01	2.5000E-01
9.1000E-01	2.5600E-01	2.3296E-01	2.4688E-01
9.2000E-01	2.5100E-01	2.3092E-01	2.4462E-01
9.3000E-01	2.4700E-01	2.2971E-01	2.4130E-01
9.4000E-01	2.4300E-01	2.2842E-01	2.3786E-01

u	W(u)	uW(u)	Z(u)
9.5000E-01	2.3900E-01	2.2705E-01	2.3431E-01
9.6000E-01	2.3500E-01	2.2560E-01	2.3234E-01
9.7000E-01	2.3100E-01	2.2407E-01	2.3030E-01
9.8000E-01	2.2700E-01	2.2246E-01	2.2819E-01
9.9000E-01	2.2300E-01	2.2077E-01	2.2601E-01
1.0000E+00	2.1900E-01	2.1900E-01	2.2374E-01
1.1000E+00	1.8600E-01	2.0460E-01	1.9892E-01
1.2000E+00	1.5800E-01	1.8960E-01	1.7722E-01
1.3000E+00	1.3500E-01	1.7550E-01	1.6296E-01
1.4000E+00	1.1600E-01	1.6240E-01	1.4655E-01
1.5000E+00	1.0000E-01	1.5000E-01	1.3000E-01
1.6000E+00	8.6000E-02	1.3760E-01	1.1628E-01
1.7000E+00	7.5000E-02	1.2750E-01	1.0667E-01
1.8000E+00	6.5000E-02	1.1700E-01	9.2310E-02
1.9000E+00	5.6000E-02	1.0640E-01	8.7500E-02
2.0000E+00	4.9000E-02	9.8000E-02	8.1630E-02
2.1000E+00	4.3000E-02	9.0300E-02	8.1400E-02
2.2000E+00	3.7000E-02	8.1400E-02	7.5680E-02
2.3000E+00	3.3000E-02	7.5900E-02	6.9700E-02
2.4000E+00	2.8000E-02	6.7200E-02	6.7860E-02
2.5000E+00	2.5000E-02	6.2500E-02	4.0000E-02
2.6000E+00	2.2000E-02	5.7200E-02	4.5450E-02
2.7000E+00	1.9000E-02	5.1300E-02	5.2630E-02
2.8000E+00	1.7000E-02	4.7600E-02	5.8820E-02
2.9000E+00	1.5000E-02	4.3500E-02	6.6670E-02
3.0000E+00	1.3000E-02	3.9000E-02	7.6920E-02
3.1000E+00	1.1000E-02	3.4100E-02	*9.0910E-02
3.2000E+00	1.0000E-02	3.2000E-02	1.0000E-01
3.3000E+00	9.0000E-03	2.9700E-02	1.1111E-01
3.4000E+00	8.0000E-03	2.7200E-02	1.2500E-01
3.5000E+00	7.0000E-03	2.4500E-02	1.4286E-01
3.6000E+00	6.0000E-03	2.1600E-02	1.6667E-01
3.7000E+00	5.0000E-03	1.8500E-02	2.0000E-01
3.8000E+00	5.0000E-03	1.9000E-02	2.0408E-01
3.9000E+00	4.0000E-03	1.5600E-02	2.2222E-01
4.0000E+00	4.0000E-03	1.6000E-02	2.5000E-01
4.1000E+00	3.0000E-03	1.2300E-02	2.5641E-01
4.2000E+00	3.0000E-03	1.2600E-02	2.8571E-01
4.3000E+00	3.0000E-03	1.2900E-02	3.3333E-01
4.4000E+00	2.0000E-03	8.8000E-03	3.5714E-01
4.5000E+00	2.0000E-03	9.0000E-03	3.8462E-01
4.6000E+00	2.0000E-03	9.2000E-03	4.3478E-01
4.7000E+00	2.0000E-03	9.4000E-03	5.0000E-01
4.8000E+00	1.0000E-03	4.8000E-03	5.2632E-01
4.9000E+00	1.0000E-03	4.9000E-03	6.6667E-01
5.0000E+00	1.0000E-03	5.0000E-03	1.0000E+00

* Value where a double function approximately begins. Do not
  select values below these limits for uW(u) and Z(u) analysis
  (do not descend down the column beyond these limits).

APPENDIX B

CONVERSION FACTORS

HYDRAULIC CONDUCTIVITY

MULTIPLY	BY	TO OBTAIN
cm / s	21200	gpd / ft^2
cm / s	2830	ft / day
cm / s	864	m / day
ft / day	.000353	cm / s
ft / day	7.48	gpd / ft^2
ft / day	.305	m / day
gpd / ft^2	4.73 x 10^{-5}	cm / s
gpd / ft^2	.134	ft / day
gpd / ft^2	.041	m / day
m / day	.00116	cm / s
m / day	24.5	gpd / ft^2
m / day	3.28	ft / day

TRANSMISSIVITY

gpd / ft	.134	ft^2 / day
gpd / ft	.0124	m^2 / day
ft^2 / day	7.48	gpd / ft
ft^2 / day	.0929	m^2 / day
m^2 / day	10.76	ft^2 / day
m^2 / day	80.5	gpd / ft

FLOW RATES or DISCHARGE or PUMPING RATES

MULTIPLY	BY	TO OBTAIN
gpm	1440	gpd
gpm	0.1337	ft³ / min
gpm	0.0023	ft³ / sec
gpm	0.0630915	L /sec
gpm	5.348	m³ / day
gpm	0.00379	m³ / min
gpm	6.3×10^{-5}	m³ / sec
gpd	6.94×10^{-4}	gpm
gpd	0.1337	ft³ / day
gpd	9.28×10^{-5}	ft³ / min
gpd	1.55×10^{-6}	ft³ / sec
gpd	4.38×10^{-5}	L / sec
gpd	0.00379	m³ / day
gpd	2.63×10^{-6}	m³ / min
gpd	4.381×10^{-8}	m³ / sec
ft³ / day	0.00519	gpm
ft³ / day	7.48	gpd
ft³ / day	6.96×10^{-4}	ft³ / min
ft³ / day	1.16×10^{-5}	ft³ / sec
ft³ / day	3.28×10^{-4}	L /sec
ft³ / day	0.02832	m³ / day
ft³ / day	1.97×10^{-5}	m³ / min
ft³ / day	3.28×10^{-7}	m³ / sec
ft³ / min	7.48	gpm

MULTIPLY	BY	TO OBTAIN
ft³ / min	10775.6	gpd
ft³ / min	0.0167	ft³ / sec
ft³ / min	0.472	L / sec
ft³ / min	40.75	m³ / day
ft³ / min	0.0283	m³ / min
ft³ / min	4.72×10^{-4}	m³ / sec
ft³ / sec	449	gpm
ft³ / sec	646317	gpd
ft³ / sec	60	ft³ / min
ft³ / sec	28.33	L / sec
ft³ / sec	2447	m³ / day
ft³ / sec	1.70	m³ / min
ft³ / sec	0.0283	m³ / sec
L / sec	15.85	gpm
L / sec	22824	gpd
L / sec	3051.2	ft³ / day
L /sec	2.118	ft³ / min
L /sec	0.0353	ft³ / sec
L /sec	86.4	m³ / day
L / sec	0.06	m³ / min
L / sec	.001	m³ / sec
m³ / day	.1835	gpm
m³ / day	264.17	gpd
m³ / day	35.32	ft³ / day
m³ / day	0.0245	ft³ / min
m³ / day	4.088×10^{-4}	ft³ / sec

MULTIPLY	BY	TO OBTAIN
m^3 / day	0.011574	L / sec
m^3 / day	6.94×10^{-4}	m^3 / min
m^3 / day	1.1574×10^{-5}	m^3 / sec
m^3 / min	264	gpm
m^3 / min	380228	gpd
m^3 / min	1440	ft^3 / day
m^3 / min	35.3	ft^3 / min
m^3 / min	0.588	ft^3 / sec
m^3 / min	16.67	L /sec
m^3 / min	1440	m^3 / day
m^3 / min	0.0167	m^3 / sec
m^3 / sec	15800	gpm
m^3 / sec	2.2752×10^7	gpd
m^3 / sec	2120	ft^3 / min
m^3 / sec	35.3	ft^3 / sec
m^3 / sec	1000	L / sec
m^3 / sec	86400	m^3 / day
m^3 / sec	60	m^3 / min

APPENDIX C

DERIVATIONS

Ogden's uW(u) Solution (1965)

Ogden equated the Theis equations for $T = gpd / ft$ and $t = days$

$$\frac{114.6Q}{s}W(u) = \frac{1.87Sr^2}{ut} \qquad (1\text{-}C)$$

and arrived at

$$uW(u) = \frac{1.87Sr^2}{114.6Qt}, \qquad (2\text{-}C)$$

which can be used with a storage assumption and

$$T = \frac{1.87Sr^2}{ut}. \qquad (3\text{-}C)$$

Sheahan's Z(u) Equation (1967)

Sheahan substituted the value uW(u) from equation (2-C) into

$$2Z(u) = \frac{2uW(2u)}{uW(u)} = \frac{2W(2u)}{W(u)} \qquad (4\text{-}C)$$

to arrive at

$$Z(u) = \frac{s_{1/2t}}{s_t} = \frac{W(2u)}{W(u)}. \qquad (5\text{-}C)$$

Kasenow's t'_o Equation (1993)

Using the Cooper-Jacob approximation equation...

$$\Delta s = \frac{264Q}{T} = \frac{s_2 - s_1}{\log \frac{t_2}{t_1}} \qquad (6\text{-}C)$$

and rearranging the first and third terms results in

$$s_{new} = s_{old} + [(\Delta s) \log (t_{new} / t_{old})] = ft, \text{ and} \qquad (7\text{-}C)$$

$$\log t_{new} = \frac{s_{new} - s_{old}}{\Delta s} + \log t_{old}, \text{ take the antilog} = t_{new} = min. \qquad (8\text{-}C)$$

When $t_o = t_{new}$, then $s_{new} = 0$, and

$$\log t_{new} = \frac{- s_{old}}{\Delta s} + \log t_{old}, \text{ take the antilog} = t_o = min. \qquad (9\text{-}C)$$

Assume $\Delta s' = \Delta s'_{rec}$, and use equation (8-C) with recovery data:

$$\frac{s_{rec2} - s_{rec1}}{\Delta s'} + \log t_{rec1} = \log t'_o, \text{ take the antilog} = t'_o = min. \qquad (8\text{-}C)$$

Setting $s_{rec2} = 0$, results in equation (10-C) [remember $s_{rec} = (s - s')$]:

$$- \frac{s_{rec1}}{\Delta s'} + \log t' = - \frac{(s - s')}{\Delta s'} + \log t' = \log t'_o \qquad (10\text{-}C)$$

take the antilog $= t'_o = min.$

s' is the residual drawdown in feet at time, t', in minutes.

s is the theoretical extended drawdown for the pump test if it had continued (graph 2, Figure 9).

s' at t', and $\Delta s'$ can be identified from the residual drawdown graph.

Only s or s_{new} needs to be defined in order to calculate t'_o.

A variation of equation (7-C) can be used to predict the theoretical drawdown, s or s_{new}:

$$s_{new} = s_{old} + [(\Delta s) \log (t_{new}/ t_{old})] = \text{ft} \qquad (7\text{-}C)$$

$$s_{new} = s_{off} + [\Delta s' [\log((t_{off} + t') / (t_{off}))]] . \qquad (11\text{-}C)$$

Recovery $(s - s')$ can then be described by equation (12-C):

$$s_{rec} = (s - s') = (s_{new} - s')$$

$$s_{rec1} = s_{off} + [\Delta s' [\log((t_{off} + t') / (t_{off}))]] - s' , \qquad (12\text{-}C)$$

where s_{off} = the drawdown immediately after the pumping well has been turned off (or last transient drawdown),

$\Delta s'$ = the slope of the residual drawdown graph,

t_{off} = time duration of pump test (or of last transient drawdown),

s' = the residual drawdown, and

t' = time since pump was turned off relative to s'.

C-3

Then substitute equation (12-C) into equation (10-C):

$$s_{rec1} = s_{off} + [\Delta s' [\log((t_{off} + t') / (t_{off}))]] - s' \qquad (12\text{-}C)$$

$$-\frac{s_{rec1}}{\Delta s'} + \log t' = -\frac{(s - s')}{\Delta s'} + \log t' = \log t'_o \qquad (10\text{-}C)$$

take the antilog $= t'_o =$ min.

The final result is equation (13-C),

$$-\frac{[s_{off} + [\Delta s' [\log ((t_{off} + t') / (t_{off}))]] - s']}{\Delta s'} + \log t' \qquad (13\text{-}C)$$

$= \log t'_o$ <u>Can be used with late s' and</u>

take the antilog   <u>t' data that fall on or are</u>

$= t'_o =$ minutes.   <u>directly adjacent to $\Delta s'$.</u>

Use the Cooper-Jacob approximation to calculate S,

$$S = \frac{0.3Tt'_o}{r^2}, \qquad (14\text{-}C)$$

where

T = transmissivity = gpd /ft
t'_o = time of zero recovery = days
r = the observation well distance = feet.

CALCULATING t'_o AND THE STORAGE COEFFICIENT USING RESIDUAL DRAWDOWN DATA

(13-C) $\log t'_o = -[[s_{off} + [\Delta s' [\log ((t_{off} + t') / (t_{off}))]] - s'] / \Delta s'] + \log t' \longrightarrow$ antilog $= t'_o$, min

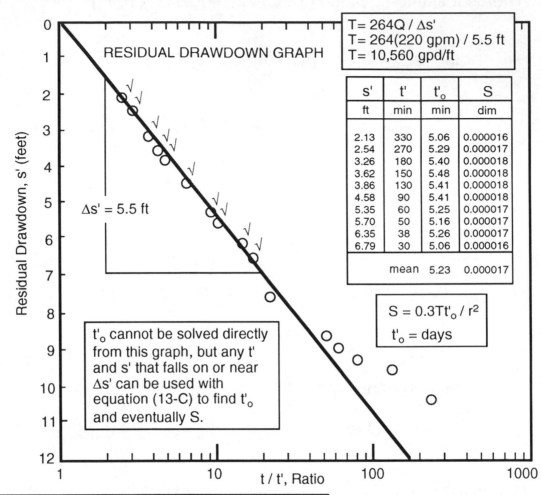

RESIDUAL DRAWDOWN GRAPH

$\Delta s' = 5.5$ ft

t'_o cannot be solved directly from this graph, but any t' and s' that falls on or near $\Delta s'$ can be used with equation (13-C) to find t'_o and eventually S.

$T = 264Q / \Delta s'$
$T = 264(220 \text{ gpm}) / 5.5 \text{ ft}$
$T = 10,560$ gpd/ft

s'	t'	t'_o	S
ft	min	min	dim
2.13	330	5.06	0.000016
2.54	270	5.29	0.000017
3.26	180	5.40	0.000018
3.62	150	5.48	0.000018
3.86	130	5.41	0.000018
4.58	90	5.41	0.000018
5.35	60	5.25	0.000017
5.70	50	5.16	0.000017
6.35	38	5.26	0.000017
6.79	30	5.06	0.000016
	mean	5.23	0.000017

$S = 0.3Tt'_o / r^2$
$t'_o =$ days

Residual Drawdown, s' (feet)

t / t', Ratio

Time since pump test started t, min	Time since pumping stopped t', min	Ratio, t/t'	Residual drawdown s', ft
500[1]	0	----	10.9[2]
502	2	251	10.6
504	4	126	9.70
506	6	84	9.60
508	8	63.5	9.10
510	10	51	8.81
520	20	26	7.76
530	30	17.67	6.79
538	38	14.16	6.35
550	50	11	5.70
560	60	9.33	5.35
590	90	6.56	4.58
630	130	4.85	3.86
650	150	4.33	3.62
680	180	3.78	3.26
770	270	2.85	2.54
830	330	2.52	2.13

<u>Data compiled from Bruin and Hudson (1955):</u>

Q = 220 gpm, r = 824 ft, t = 500 min

<u>Pump Test Results (Bruin and Hudson,1955):</u>

T = 10,950 gpd/ft; S = 0.000017

<u>Pump Test Results (Walton, 1962):</u>

10,100 gpd/ft; S = 0.00002

<u>Recovery Results (Bruin and Hudson,1955):</u>

T = 10,950 gpd/ft; S = 0.000017

t'_o from the recovery graph constructed by Bruin and Hudson = 5.1 min = 0.00354 days

[1]t_{off} [2]s_{off}

FIGURE 22

C-5

EQUATIONS USED IN THE THEIS WITHOUT GRAPHS
COMPUTER PROGRAM

The Δs using <u>time - drawdown</u> data can be rewritten as

$$\Delta s \;=\; \frac{264Q}{T} \;=\; \frac{s_2 - s_1}{\log \frac{t_2}{t_1}} \qquad\qquad (15\text{-}C)$$

and

$$\Delta s \;=\; s_2 - s_1, \text{ when the } \log (t_2 / t_1) \;=\; 1 \text{ or when computed over one complete log cycle.}$$

The Δs using <u>distance drawdown</u> data can be rewritten as

$$\Delta s \;=\; \frac{528Q}{T} \;=\; \frac{s_2 - s_1}{\log \frac{r_1}{r_2}} \qquad\qquad (16\text{-}C)$$

and

$$\Delta s \;=\; s_2 - s_1, \text{ when the } \log (r_1 / r_2) \;=\; 1 \text{ or when computed over one complete log cycle.}$$

where

$s_2 - s_1$ = the difference between two drawdowns over

the log of the quotient of two times = $\log (t_2 / t_1)$ or

the log of the quotient of two distances = $\log (r_1 / r_2)$.

T = transmissivity = gpd / ft.

Q = pumping rate = gpm.

Rearrange equation (15-C) to find t_o:

$$\log t_o = \frac{s_2 - s_1}{\Delta s} + \log t_1, \text{ take the antilog} = t_o, \qquad (17\text{-}C)$$

and because $s_2 = 0$,

$$\log t_o = \frac{-s_1}{\Delta s} + \log t_1, \text{ take the antilog} = t_o. \qquad (18\text{-}C)$$

Using the same logic, but for zero drawdown relative to the distance drawdown graph:

$$\log r_o = \frac{\pm s_1}{2\Delta s} + \log r_1, \text{ take the antilog} = r_o. \qquad (19\text{-}C)$$

(+) by convention, because the slope is constructed into the opposite direction. r_1 = the observation well distance.

The theoretical drawdown in the pumping well (s_p) can be estimated using

$$s_p = (2\Delta s) \log (r_o / r_w) \qquad (20\text{-}C)$$

where r_w = radius of the pumping well.

Assuming $r_w = 1.00$ ft,

$$s_p = (2\Delta s)\log(r_o). \qquad (21\text{-}C)$$

The theoretical specific capacity can be estimated using

$$Q / s_p = \text{gallons per minute / foot of drawdown} = \text{gpm / ft.}$$

In addition, the drawdown at any time can be predicted by rearranging equation (15-C):

$$s_{new} = s_{old} + [(\Delta s) \log (t_{new} / t_{old})] \qquad (22\text{-}C)$$

$$s_{new} = s_{old} + [[(s_2 - s_1) / \log (t_2 / t_1)]\log (t_{new} / t_{old})] \qquad (23\text{-}C)$$

$$s_{new} = s_{old} + [[(264Q) / T] \log (t_{new} / t_{old})] = \text{ft.} \qquad (24\text{-}C)$$

The time at which a drawdown will occur can be predicted by rearranging equation (15-C):

$$\log t_{new} = \frac{s_{new} - s_{old}}{\Delta s} + \log t_{old}, \text{ take the antilog } = t_{new} \qquad (25\text{-}C)$$

$$\log t_{new} = \frac{s_{new} - s_{old}}{\dfrac{s_2 - s_1}{\log \dfrac{t_2}{t_1}}} + \log t_{old}, \text{ take the antilog } = t_{new} \qquad (26\text{-}C)$$

$$\log t_{new} = \frac{s_{new} - s_{old}}{\dfrac{264Q}{T}} + \log t_{old}, \text{ take the antilog } = t_{new} \qquad (27\text{-}C)$$

where

s_{new} = new drawdown at the desired time, t_{new},
s_{old} = old or current drawdown at the the old or current time, t_{old},
Δs = the change in drawdown over one log cycle = slope,
Q = pumping rate = gpm,
T = transmissivity = gpd / ft,
s_2, s_1, t_2 and t_1 are drawdowns and respective times.

Equation (16-C) can also be rearranged to find t_o:

$$\log t_o = \frac{s_2 - s_1}{\Delta s / 2} + \log t_1, \text{ take the antilog} = t_o \qquad (28\text{-}C)$$

and because $s_2 = 0$,

$$\log t_o = \frac{-s_1}{\Delta s / 2} + \log t_1, \text{ take the antilog} = t_o. \qquad (29\text{-}C)$$

Using the same logic, but for zero drawdown relative to the distance drawdown data:

$$\log r_o = \frac{\pm s_1}{\Delta s} + \log r_1, \text{ take the antilog} = r_o. \qquad (30\text{-}C)$$

(+) by convention, because the slope is constructed into the opposite direction. $r_1 = $ the observation well distance.

The theoretical drawdown in the pumping well (s_p) can be estimated using

$$s_p = (\Delta s) \log (r_o / r_w) \qquad (31\text{-}C)$$

where $r_w = $ radius of the pumping well.

Assuming $r_w = 1.00$ ft,

$$s_p = (\Delta s) \log (r_o). \qquad (32\text{-}C)$$

The theoretical specific capacity can be estimated using

$$Q / s_p = \text{gallons per minute / foot of drawdown} = \text{gpm / ft.}$$

In addition, the drawdown at any distance can be predicted by rearranging equation (16-C):

$$s_{new} = s_{old} + [(\Delta s) \log (r_{old} / r_{new})] \qquad \text{(33-C)}$$

$$s_{new} = s_{old} + [[(s_2 - s_1) / \log (r_1 / r_2)] \log (r_{old} / r_{new})] \qquad \text{(34-C)}$$

$$s_{new} = s_{old} + [[(528Q) / T] \log (r_{old} / r_{new})] = \text{ft.} \qquad \text{(35-C)}$$

The distance at which a drawdown will occur can be predicted by rearranging equation (16-C):

$$\log r_{new} = \frac{s_{old} - s_{new}}{\Delta s} + \log r_{old}, \text{ take the antilog} = r_{new} \qquad \text{(36-C)}$$

$$\log r_{new} = \frac{s_{old} - s_{new}}{\dfrac{s_2 - s_1}{\log \dfrac{r_1}{r_2}}} + \log r_{old}, \text{ take the antilog} = r_{new} \qquad \text{(37-C)}$$

$$\log r_{new} = \frac{s_{old} - s_{new}}{\dfrac{528Q}{T}} + \log r_{old}, \text{ take the antilog} = r_{new} = \text{ft}, \qquad \text{(38-C)}$$

where

s_{new} = new drawdown at the desired time, r_{new},
s_{old} = old or current drawdown at the the old or current time, r_{old},
Δs = the change in drawdown over one log cycle = slope,
Q = pumping rate = gpm, and
T = transmissivity = gpd / ft.
s_2, s_1, r_2 and r_1 are drawdowns and respective distances.

r_o predicted using specific capacity data, (Q/s), can be simplified even further when r_1 is assumed to be 1.0 ft, because,

$s_2 = 0$ and $\log r_1$ at 1 ft $= 0$; therefore,

$$\log r_o = \frac{+s_1}{\Delta s} = \text{take the antilog,} = r_o = \text{ft} \qquad (39\text{-C})$$

where

Δs = to the slope of the distance - drawdown graph = ft, and
s_1 = the specific capacity drawdown = ft.

When using the Δs from a time-drawdown graph and specific capacity data, equation (39-C) can be adjusted to

$$\log r_o = \frac{+s_1}{2\Delta s} = \text{take the antilog,} = r_o = \text{ft.} \qquad (40\text{-C})$$